1999

D1479321

Legal Guide for Long-Term Care Administrators

Peter J. Buttaro, MSHA, JD, FACHE
Attorney at Law
Aberdeen, South Dakota

Emily L. H. Buttaro
Editor

AN ASPEN PUBLICATION®
Aspen Publishers, Inc.
Gaithersburg, Maryland
1999

Library of Congress Cataloging-in-Publication Data

Buttaro, Peter J.
Legal guide for long-term care administrators / Peter J. Buttaro : Emily L.H. Buttaro, editor
p. cm.
Includes bibliographical references and index.
ISBN 0-8342-1370-2 (alk. paper)
1. Nursing homes—Law and legislation—United States. 2. Long-term care facilities—Law and legislation—United States. 3. Nursing home care—United States. 4. Long-term care of the sick—United States. I. Buttaro, Emily L.H. II. Title.
KF3826.N8B88   1999
344.73'03216—dc21
99-32771
CIP

Aspen Publishers, Inc., grants permission for photocopying for limited personal or internal use. This consent does not extend to other kinds of copying, such as copying for general distribution, for advertising or promotional purposes, for creating new collective works, or for resale. For information, address Aspen Publishers, Inc., Permissions Department, 200 Orchard Ridge Drive, Suite 200, Gaithersburg, Maryland 20878.

Orders: (800) 638-8437
Customer Service: (800) 234-1660

About Aspen Publishers • For more than 35 years, Aspen has been a leading professional publisher in a variety of disciplines. Aspen's vast information resources are available in both print and electronic formats. We are committed to providing the highest quality information available in the most appropriate format for our customers. Visit Aspen's Internet site for more information resources, directories, articles, and a searchable version of Aspen's full catalog, including the most recent publications: **http://www.aspenpublishers.com**
Aspen Publishers, Inc. • The hallmark of quality in publishing
Member of the worldwide Wolters Kluwer group.

Editorial Services: Kathleen Ruby
Library of Congress Catalog Card Number: 99-32771
ISBN: 0-8342-1370-2

Printed in the United States of America

1 2 3 4 5

TABLE OF CONTENTS

INTRODUCTION

As chief executive officer, the administrator of a long-term health care facility should be aware of the legal concepts pertaining to its operation. Knowledge of the basic legal concepts enables the administrator to assist the governing body in establishing rules and regulations of a legal preventive nature.

The cases in this *Legal Guide* have been researched and updated to reflect the current law; cases with older dates are also current law. In the long-term health care field, many principles of law that pertain in hospital settings apply directly to assisted living, nursing and skilled nursing facility settings as well.

This practical guide is not intended as a legal research tool. It is intended to assist the practicing administrator to become familiar with the law applying to the operation of a long-term care facility.

CHAPTER 1

Review of the Judiciary System

A law is a rule of conduct that society enforces for the common good of a group of people. The law determines the rights of members of the society and the obligations owed to that society. There are five basic divisions of law: common, statutory, criminal, civil, and administrative.

Common Law

Common law is passed down as a result of court decisions. In the Middle Ages, laws were primarily customs of society handed down from generation to generation. Today, common law is not enunciated in writing but results from many legal decisions. A court, in interpreting a set of facts, may come to a conclusion in a case based upon such customary law. The use of precedent case law (common law) is termed *stare decises* (following the decisions).

Statutory Law

Statutory law is made or enacted by the Congress of the United States, state legislatures, and other legislative bodies (counties, townships, municipalities, etc.). Statutory law is written, published, and made available to the public; it is binding upon every person. These laws usually are formal and codified according to subject matter areas—for example, contracts, corporation law, tort law.

Criminal Law

Criminal law involves violations against society or the public as a whole. It performs several functions. It punishes violators of the law for their activities by imposing sanctions (punitive measures). It restrains violators by placing them in prisons. It can perform a rehabilitative function by helping the criminal to become a useful member of society. The enforcement of criminal law is the job of the federal, state, or municipal government. The governmental subdivision becomes the plaintiff and is represented by the prosecuting attorney.

Civil Law

Civil law is concerned with conduct between individuals. There are several functions of civil law: to settle disputes in a fair, consistent, and impartial manner; to make sure that the judgments of the court are honored; and to provide a mechanism for a peaceable settlement of disputes. Thus, the primary purpose of civil law is to obtain satisfaction for the wrong committed by the defendant by awarding liquidated damages or money to the plaintiff. It is not to place the wrongdoer in jail or to fine him or her, as in a criminal case. The government is not a party to the action; the cause of action is started by a private person who seeks redress for wrongs. The party bringing the action is the plaintiff, and the party against whom the action is brought is the defendant.

Civil law is subdivided into two types of actions. Today, both actions are usually initiated in a single court.

1. *Actions at law*—When redress is sought for money damages, the action is an action at law—for example, when a plaintiff sues a nursing facility for negligence and seeks money damages or a money judgment against the facility for a wrongful act.
2. *Actions in equity*—This type of action involves the seeking of a restraining order or an order to compel, compelling another to refrain from some activity that adversely affects the plaintiff's interests—for example, when nurses threaten to go on strike illegally, a facility may seek a restraining order to prevent them from doing so. If the nurses

have already walked out of the facility illegally, the facility can seek a writ of mandamus to compel the nurses to return to work.

Some common areas of civil law affecting long-term care facility administrators in their work are:

- **tort law**—relating to such wrongs as negligence, malpractice, defamation, assault and battery, and false imprisonment
- **sales law**—relating to the purchase and sale of personal property
- **contract law**—relating to verbal and written agreements
- **probate law**—relating to administration of estates and guardianships
- **real estate law**—relating to purchase or sale of real property

Administrative Law

Administrative law is created by administrative or regulatory agencies in the form of rules, regulations, orders, and decisions to carry out their regulatory powers and duties. The agencies are delegated authority by the state or federal legislatures to adopt regulations. To be legally enforceable, these regulations must be within the scope of each administrative agency's authority and consistent with the statute that created it.

Regulations resemble statutes but are published by administrative agencies—generally, to implement statutes. Regulatory agencies on the federal level include the Department of Health and Human Services (HHS), the Internal Revenue Service (IRS), the Department of the Treasury, and the Food and Drug Administration (FDA). Agencies on the state level include state health departments and licensing agencies. The Board of Examiners for Nursing Home Administrators is a state administrative agency with which most licensed administrators are familiar.

Long-term care administrators should be familiar with the following terms:

- **administrative acts**—acts necessary to carry out the legislative policies and purposes already declared by the legislative body
- **administrative agency**—governmental body charged with administering and implementing particular legislation

- **administrative board**—body with a variety of functions involving orders, rules, or other acts made after a required notice and hearing or where full hearing is not required
- **administrative crime**—a violation of an administrative rule or regulation that carries with it criminal sanction
- **administrative hearing**—an oral proceeding consisting of arguments or a trial before an administrative agency—for example, a hearing before the Licensing Board of Examiners for Nursing Home Administrators
- **administrative law judge**—one who presides at an administrative hearing with power to take testimony, rule on questions of evidence, and make agency determination of facts. Usually, decisions by an administrative law judge may be appealed to a state higher court
- **administrative procedures act**—describes the procedures under which federal administrative agencies must operate

HCFA Survey Procedures

Within the realm of administrative law important to the long-term care industry is the accurate interpretation of the rules and regulations that are vital to the development and implementation of the Omnibus Budget Reconciliation Act (OBRA) 1987, 1989, 1990, and 1991. Skilled nursing and nursing facilities are required to be in compliance with Code of Federal Regulations (CFR) Part 483, Subpart B. An OBRA survey is a resident-centered inspection of a facility that relies on case-mix sampling of residents to see that compliance exists. The responsible administrative agency, Health Care Financing Administration (HCFA), has divided the survey process into seven tasks.

1. off-site survey preparation
2. entrance conference
3. initial tour
4. sample selection
5. information gathering
6. information analysis for deficiency determination
7. exit conference

The survey team evaluates the inspection results and evidence gathered to determine if the facility is in substantial compliance with the CFR or if a deficiency exists where the facility has failed to meet one of the specified participation requirements. When a facility is in substantial compliance but has isolated deficiencies causing no actual harm, the surveyors include the deficiencies on a notice of isolated deficiencies.

If the survey team finds that a facility is not in compliance and a deficiency exists, it assesses the effect on the resident's outcome (severity level) and determines the number of additional residents potentially or actually affected (scope level).

There are four severity levels.

1. Level 1—Deficiency has the potential for causing no more than minimal harm.
2. Level 2—Noncompliance has resulted in minimal discomfort to the resident.
3. Level 3—Noncompliance has resulted in a negative outcome that has compromised the resident's ability to reach the highest physical, mental, and psychological well-being.
4. Level 4—Immediate corrective action is necessary. Noncompliance has caused or is likely to cause serious injury, harm, impairment, or death. This level has three scopes: isolated, pattern, and widespread.

The scope level of a deficiency is determined by evaluating the cause of the deficiency. The survey team examines to see if the facility has a policy in the deficient area, if the policy is adequate, or if an existing policy is not being followed adequately to meet the requirements. If failure to have a relative policy has potential to affect a large number of residents, the deficient practice may be *widespread*. If a policy is in place but not adequately implemented, the deficient practice is likely to be considered a *pattern*. If the deficient practice affects a limited number of residents, the scope is *isolated*.

Once the severity and scope of the deficiency have been ascertained, the survey team must find out if the quality of care is substandard and determine if the resident is in immediate jeopardy. Immediate jeopardy is a situation where the facility's failure to meet one or more requirements of participation has caused or may cause serious injury, harm, impairment, or the death of a resident. The statement of deficiencies identifies the specific content of each requirement that is not met.

The three categories of remedies for the deficiencies are:

1. **Category I**—directed plan of correction, state monitoring, or directed inservice training
2. **Category II**—denial of payment for new admissions, denial of payment for all residents, or civil monetary fees of $50 to $3,000 per day
3. **Category III**—temporary management, immediate termination from Medicare and Medicaid programs, or civil monetary penalties of $3,050 to $10,000 per day

THE COURT SYSTEM IN THE UNITED STATES

The court system is broadly divided into the federal court system and the state court system. Jurisdiction is defined as the power of a court to inquire into the facts of a case, to apply the law, and to declare judgments. For a court to hear a case, it must have jurisdiction over the subject matter of the dispute.

Federal Court System

The federal courts are created by the United States Congress to administer the laws they enact. The jurisdiction of these courts is found in Article III of the United States Constitution, which provides for the creation of federal courts to hear certain types of law cases. Generally, federal courts hear cases of a federal nature stemming from federal law, controversies between two states, civil matters involving private citizens who reside in different states, and disputes involving a violation of federal criminal statutes. These courts have exclusive power to hear cases of an antitrust nature or involving securities.

The federal court system is divided into three courts.

1. **United States District Court**—This is a trial court of the federal system and hears disputes of a civil and criminal nature. Trials concerning violations of federal laws, bankruptcy, and cases between citizens of different states are heard.
2. **United States Courts of Appeals**—These courts hear appeals from the decisions of the federal district courts. Special courts within this system were created by Congress to handle special problems of a

federal nature. Some of these are the *United States Court of Claims*, which hears cases involving a breach of contract between the United States government and third parties; the *United States Customs Court*, which hears cases involving customs regulations; the *Tax Court of the United States*, which hears cases involving the IRS and individuals or corporations; and the *United States Court of Military Appeals*, which hears cases relative to individuals in the military services.

3. **United States Supreme Court**—This court has appellate jurisdiction in both federal and state disputes; it is not a trial court. It reviews such matters as appeals from a state supreme court with the view toward determining whether or not the laws passed by the state are constitutional. The Supreme Court has a great deal of discretion in determining whether or not it will hear a particular case, generally hearing those of national or far-reaching implications where the outcome of the controversy applies to a significant number of United States citizens.

State Court System

The state courts are created by the individual state legislatures and generally differ with each state. A broad division of these courts includes:

- **Magistrate court**—This trial court has jurisdiction over misdemeanors, minor traffic accidents, small claims, and preliminary hearings regarding felony violations.

- **State circuit court**—This court has trial jurisdiction over more serious litigation involving matters of a criminal and civil nature. In the criminal law area, it hears all felonies. In the civil law area, it hears malpractice, negligence, breach of contract, condemnation, and violations and disputes involving state laws passed by their legislatures. This court is empowered to hear probate matters (wills, administration of estates, appointment of guardians, adoption and juvenile procedures) and divorce cases.

- **State court of appeals**—Not all states have an intermediate court of appeals. A court of appeals normally hears only those cases appealed from the state circuit court within the state system. It is not a trial court and usually does not have original jurisdiction to conduct trials.

- **State supreme court**—This court does not usually have trial jurisdiction but hears cases appealed from state circuit courts or state courts of appeals. This is the court of last resort in the state system, and its findings regarding state laws and other matters are binding on all citizens of the particular state. Controversies may be appealed to the United States Supreme Court.

COURT PROCEDURE

A typical sequence of events that takes place in the initiation and trying of a civil case is described here.

Complaint and Summons

In the first step in a lawsuit, two documents—a complaint and a summons—are filed with the clerk of the court in the jurisdiction where the case will be tried.

- A **complaint** is a document drafted by the attorney for the plaintiff, prepared after consultation with the client. Its purpose is to provide the defendant with formal notification of the lawsuit. The essential elements of the cause of action must be clearly stated. For example, if a lawsuit for negligence is started against a nursing facility, the complaint must include statements of a general nature describing the legal duty owed to the plaintiff, a breach of the duty outlining the fact situation, how the injury to the plaintiff was directly caused by the breach of duty, and the damages suffered by the plaintiff with a statement of the amount of money the plaintiff wishes to receive as a result of the defendant's negligent acts.
- The **summons** is a document notifying the defendant that unless an answer to the complaint is submitted to the plaintiff within 30 days after service upon the defendant, the defendant may lose the case, and a default judgment will be entered against him or her.

Answer

The next step in the course of the law action is the filing or submission of an answer to the plaintiff's attorney by the defendant. Regardless of the justification or merits of the lawsuit, the defendant must respond or the law presumes that the plaintiff's complaint is true and may give a judgment for the plaintiff. The attorney for the defendant usually makes a general denial in the answer to the plaintiff's claim as stated in the complaint, thus placing all allegations of the complaint in issue. If the defendant chooses to admit to some allegations and deny others, only those issues denied are subject to litigation.

In addition to the general denial, the defense attorney may plead affirmative defenses (reasons why the plaintiff's legal right to bring such action should be denied) in the answer. Affirmative defenses are presumed to be waived if the defense attorney does not plead them. For example, in a negligence action, depending upon the circumstances, the defense attorney for a nursing facility may submit such affirmative defenses as contributory negligence, statute of limitations, assumption of risk, and accord and satisfaction.

Pretrial Procedures

After the answer is submitted to the plaintiff's attorney, the next step is to learn as much about the issues in the lawsuit as possible. Full disclosure of all pertinent facts by both parties helps serve the objects of justice and usually shortens the duration of the trial. In modern law cases, the element of surprise at the time of trial is minimized by the pretrial discovery procedures used by both attorneys. The common pretrial discovery methods are:

- A **deposition** is an oral examination of one or both of the parties involved and/or witnesses to the litigation. The hearing is conducted by either the attorney for the plaintiff or the attorney for the defendant. Both attorneys are usually present to make sure that the rights of their clients are protected. The attorney conducting the hearing may ask a variety of questions related to the issues being tried. The questions and answers (which are given under oath) are recorded by a court reporter. A transcript is compiled for use by both attorneys. This procedure gives both attorneys an opportunity to know what the witnesses will say at the trial, allowing time to establish or refute the answers given in the depositions. Some attorneys may use the deposition to impeach the character of a witness or a party to the action, if the answers given are substantially different from the answers given on the witness stand at time of trial.

- **Interrogatories** are written questions concerned with the facts of the case at hand that the attorney for either party may ask of the other party. The questions must be answered under oath. As with the answers to depositions, these answers may also be used as a method of impeachment of a witness or party, if the answers given at the trial are substantially different from those given in the interrogatory.

- **Pretrial conferences** may be held among the attorneys in the presence of the judge to simplify the issues in the case, discuss any necessary amendment to the complaint or answer, take admissions of either party to shorten the trial by avoiding unnecessary proof, or encourage a settlement satisfactory to both parties. Pretrial conferences can help to shorten considerably the time of trial and encourage settlement.

Civil Trial

The vital point in a lawsuit is the actual trial, which may be conducted before a judge and jury or before a judge alone. It is a basic right of the parties to a lawsuit to demand a jury trial. The judge is concerned with the issues of law and the jury is the trier of fact.

The jury trial starts with the selection of a jury. Some trial attorneys maintain that the selection of the jury is one of the most important phases of the trial. It is obvious that if the jury is not sympathetic to the case being tried, the plaintiff will not prevail.

After the selection of the jury, the plaintiff's attorney is given an opportunity to make an opening statement outlining to the jury what he or she hopes to prove in the complaint and how he or she will go about proving the allegations. The defense attorney also has an opportunity to make an opening statement. The plaintiff then proceeds to call witnesses and other parties to prove each and every element at issue. (The plaintiff's attorney must prove all elements of the action to meet the burden of proof. If the attorney does not, the case may be decided in favor of the defendant by a directed verdict without even going to the jury.) After the plaintiff calls and questions witnesses, the defense may cross-examine each. The defendant then has an opportunity to call and question his or her witnesses and/or other parties; the plaintiff's attorney may cross-examine these. (The questions put to witnesses must comply with rules of evidence for the answers to be admitted into the trial transcript.) The plaintiff's attorney makes a closing statement; the attorney for the defendant follows. Finally, the attorney for the plaintiff makes a rebuttal statement.

The trial itself is conducted by a judge. The judge's function is to present the law to the jury in plain and understandable terms (instructions). These instructions include an explanation of the applicable law and what this law requires regarding factual elements that the jury must find in the case before it can render a verdict. The instructions are given after all evidence and arguments in the case are submitted. After these instructions are given, the jury retires to render a verdict. Where there is no jury, the judge renders the verdict.

Right To Appeal

After the judge or jury renders a decision, the losing party is still afforded an important right—the right to appeal the case to a higher court. Generally, an appeal must be made on the basis of an error of law made during the proceedings, as the function of an appellate court is to consider errors of law, not to try the facts of the case again. The appellate court reviews a transcript of the case and may request legal briefs outlining the legal arguments as to why the decision should or should not stand. In examining this record, the court looks to see if evidence is sufficient to sustain the decision. A verdict based upon prejudice, a wrong interpretation, or other error in the record may reverse the lower court's decision or remand the case for a new trial.

It is important to remember the distinction between findings of fact and conclusions of law. The findings of fact made by the jury or judge are based on an evaluation of the evidence and testimony admitted into the case. The conclusions of law are based upon an accurate interpretation of the application of the law to the case. Any case that is appealed is based on error of law.

BURDEN OF PROOF

The burden of proof is upon the plaintiff throughout the entire lawsuit in both civil and criminal proceedings.

In a civil case, the plaintiff must show by a preponderance of evidence that he or she should recover from the defendant. The plaintiff must present sufficient evidence so that the jury or judge believes that his or her evidence outweighs that of the defendant. At the beginning of a trial, the plaintiff puts in evidence to sustain the case. If the defendant fails to introduce evidence to refute this evidence, he or she may lose the case by directed verdict in favor of the plaintiff.

For example, in a simple contract action for money owed, a plaintiff may testify that the defendant orally agreed to pay him for services rendered; upon reliance of this promise, he performed the services and has not received payment to date. The defendant must present proof of facts to contradict the plaintiff's evidence or offer other satisfactory defense. If this is done to the satisfaction of the jury or judge, the conclusion that the plaintiff was not entitled to the verdict as a matter of law is warranted; the case is then submitted to the jury or judge for a decision regarding the fact situation. If the defendant does not present satisfactory defense or contradiction of the plaintiff's evidence, the plaintiff is entitled to a directed verdict in his favor.

In a criminal case, the burden of proof is greater. The prosecutor (plaintiff) must prove his or her allegations beyond a reasonable doubt.

EVIDENCE

The health care facility administrator should be familiar, in a general way, with the law of evidence and the conduct of individuals who serve as witnesses in a legal procedure.

The whole idea of a legal action is to determine truth and administer justice. Evidence is material introduced into a trial that tends to prove to the judge or jury the truth of the issues being determined. Evidence may be introduced by general or expert witnesses, by documents or records, and by concrete objects, and must pertain to the issues being tried.

Rules of Evidence

All states have statutes dealing with the rules and regulations regarding the kind of evidence allowed in a trial and make every effort to protect the rights of all parties and witnesses to a law action. Evidence that does not comply with the state rules is not allowed into the proceedings by the court. Rules of evidence that are important to the testimony given by persons appearing in court are discussed below.

Opinion Evidence

One of the basic rules is that the information given in court be of a reliable nature. Thus, the court allows only that evidence based upon the opportunity of the witness to observe certain events or facts, excluding opinion. Opinion evidence regards what the witness thinks, believes, or infers in relation to the issue at hand rather than what he or she actually observed. It involves a conclusion drawn by the witness from the facts he or she knows and is, therefore, not allowed.

For example, a resident is found lying next to his bed, and he has a broken hip. A witness is asked to testify about the event. The witness observed only that the resident was lying next to his bed. However, in answer to a question, he says that the resident fell out of the bed. By making this statement, the witness has drawn a conclusion about the events rather than reporting what was actually observed.

There are exceptions to the opinion rule. For instance, a qualified expert witness may give opinion testimony.

Hearsay Evidence

Hearsay evidence is a statement by a witness that is introduced into evidence for the purpose of trying to determine the truth of the issue, of something the witness heard from a source outside of court. A basic rule is the exclusion of hearsay evidence from legal proceedings. Out-of-court utterances are generally not admissible because the source of the statement is not in court under oath, where there is opportunity for cross-examination. There are some exceptions to this rule.

Relevance of Evidence

Evidence admitted in a legal proceeding must be pertinent to the particular issue being tried. A witness's statement that tends to prove or disprove the issue is considered relevant. Statements that are not relative to the issue are not admitted into evidence.

Privileged Communication

Most states by statute do not allow written or oral communications of a confidential nature between certain prescribed parties to be admitted into evidence. Such confidential matters are *privileged communications*. A privilege is a rule of law that permits a witness to refrain from giving testimony (that he or she might otherwise have to give) in order to protect an interest or relationship. Thus, a privilege is of a personal nature and is valid only for the person whose relationship the court is trying to protect. Four conditions must be satisfied in order to have this privilege.

1. There must be an intention that the communication not be disclosed.
2. The confidentiality must be essential to the relationship.
3. It must be a relationship that desires protection.
4. Release of the information on the witness stand would cause greater harm than if the information were not released.

The common privileged communications in American civil law are between:

- **Husband and wife**—The privilege exists because the law says it is against public policy to allow spouses to testify against one another, as this would breach the trust and confidence of the marital relationship. This privilege belongs to both spouses and applies only to confidential oral or written communications made during the marriage. Neither spouse may testify against the other without his or her consent.
- **Clergyman and penitent**—A member of the clergy cannot be examined in criminal or civil proceedings as to any confidential communication made to him or her in the course of the professional relationship without the consent of the penitent. Some states limit the privilege to confessions of sin; others say that the privilege belongs only to the penitent; others say that it applies to both the member of the clergy and the penitent. In any case, either party to a legal proceeding may claim the privilege.
- **Physician and patient**—This privilege is based upon the premise that full disclosure of information between patient and physician is an aid to the treatment of illness. The rule says that a physician, surgeon, or other practitioner of healing cannot be examined as to information

learned while attending a patient in a civil action without that patient's consent. The privilege belongs to the patient or to his or her guardian, if the patient is incompetent. It does not belong to the physician, although the physician may be compelled to testify if the patient waives the privilege.

The privilege applies to communication between physician and patient and to information obtained from the patient in the course of medical examination. The principal areas where this privilege applies are in domestic relations and in actions to enforce life insurance policies. Some items—for example, diagnostic test results—in nursing facility health records, advice given to the patient, and doctor's opinions may be protected, while personal information (patient's name, address, occupation, and so on) may not be protected.

The thinking of the courts has been to limit this privilege whenever possible because little difference in medical practice is shown between states that grant the privilege and those that do not. Thus, there are many exceptions to the privilege. Courts have indicated that considerable harm is accomplished by nondisclosure of the information in the following instances:

- if the communication is one in which an illegal act takes place
- if there is a personal injury suit or wrongful death action where the issue is the extent of the plaintiff's damages
- where a question arises as to the competency of a testator in the contest of a will
- in a malpractice action against a physician
- in guardianship and commitment proceedings

A patient may waive his or her right to the privilege in a situation, such as in an insurance application containing a clause waiving this privilege. If a patient calls his or her physician to testify as a witness, the privilege is waived. If the patient testifies, the privilege may be waived.

- **Attorney and client**—The concept behind this privilege is to encourage full disclosure of all information by the client so that justice may be served. Generally stated, the rule is that an attorney cannot be examined as to any communication made by a client to him or her in the course of the professional relationship without the consent of the client. The communication must be made to a licensed attorney or to his or her agent for gathering information for the privilege to exist. The privilege may be waived by the client, an incompetent's guardian, or a deceased's personal representative. Most states recognize this privilege for criminal and civil matters.

Testimonial Evidence

Testimonial evidence is that given by a competent witness under oath. If it is proven that a witness is not telling the truth, he or she may be indicted for criminal action of perjury. Testimony is usually produced through the language of witnesses orally at trial appearances or by affidavit or deposition. Questions are asked of the witness by the attorneys involved in the lawsuit. Leading questions are not allowed unless a witness is determined weak, aged, or unfit, in which case the court may allow him or her to present a story and to be led by questions from his or her attorney. The testimony involves direct observations of a witness or expert opinions of an expert witness. Witnesses are usually used to impeach the credibility of the other witnesses and parties involved in the trial. The testimony given at a trial by witnesses in open court is subject to cross-examination by the opposing party.

Expert Witnesses and Testimony

Expert testimony is that which is given relating to professional, technical, or scientific matters by experts or other persons qualified to speak with authority on a particular subject by reason of special training, familiarity with the subject, or skill. An expert witness is an individual who has acquired an ability or peculiar knowledge by reason of skill and education not usually acquired by ordinary persons. Physicians, nurses, and technicians are considered expert in their respective areas if qualified by skill and background.

Res Ipsa Loquitor

Res ipsa loquitor is the relaxation of the requirement of expert testimony. The term literally means "the thing speaks for itself."

In a typical corporate negligence case, the standards in issue may be beyond the competence of the jury to determine without the aid of experts. However, there are cases where a jury can conclude, based on its own common sense and experience, that the injuries complained of do not happen in the absence of negligence and the doctrine of res ipsa loquitor can be applied. A typical application involves an object such as a sponge, scalpel, or other surgical instrument left in a patient's body by a surgeon. Under these circumstances, it is said that "the thing speaks for itself" and the plaintiff need not present witnesses to express opinions on matters that are obvious to a lay jury.

Generally speaking, for this doctrine to apply, three conditions must be met.

1. The event, under the circumstances of the case, does not occur in the absence of someone's negligence.
2. The event must be caused by a means within the exclusive control of the defendant.
3. The plaintiff's own actions did not contribute to the injury.

Under most state law, if these elements are established, the jury may infer that the defendant was negligent and the plaintiff need not prove the case further. In other states, there is said to be a presumption of negligence that the defendant must rebut.

Real Evidence

Real evidence is furnished by introducing an object for inspection—for example, a gun or knife used to commit a crime. If the case were one of negligence concerning medication, the medication that was improperly given could be introduced as real evidence. Documents constitute a significant category of real evidence. A nursing facility administrator is concerned with the health records of residents and business records, reports, and other transactions of the facility.

Health Record as Real Evidence

The health record of the residents in a nursing facility plays an important role in determining the quality of the care being given and may be used in a legal proceeding. As the nursing facility is a business enterprise, the health records it keeps are considered business documents kept in the course of business. The health records are original entries of people involved in resident care. They are kept current and must be complete.

State statutes require that these records be maintained as a condition of nursing facility licensure.

Generally, the health record is used to refresh the memory of a witness. Any health record offered into evidence where the person who writes the record is not a witness is considered an out-of-court assertion; it becomes inadmissible under hearsay rules. If an objection to the admission of a health record is overruled, the content of the health record is admitted if the court concludes that it is a business record applying to professions, occupations, or other business; it is admissible under the course of business rule. As the record is an account of the quality of care, diagnostic test results, and other objective findings, it is considered to have a sense of reliability.

Some of the uses of medical records in legal proceedings are:

- **In insurance cases**—With the advent of third-party prepayment for medical, hospital, and nursing facility care, the great majority of persons have health care bills paid by Blue Cross or some other commercial insurance company. The trend has been to make health care records available to those insurance companies with a vested interest in the payment of a bill.

- **In accident or personal injury cases against a nursing facility or hospital**—The plaintiff uses the medical record to show the chain of events leading up to the injury received, the extent of the injury, and the care given.

- **With the advent of federal programs (Medicare and Medicaid)**— The health record is often used to determine if the facility met the standards of participation as required by federal law and if the federal government should pay for the care of the recipient.

- **In a law action**—With the increase of personal injury suits, the parties often depend upon the health records to prove the case of the plaintiff or defend a health care facility.

- **In making a will**—There is a good probability that the nursing facility resident will make a will, which may be contested by unhappy relatives. The health care record can be used to determine the competency or incompetency of the testator at the time the will was executed.

- **In workers' compensation cases**—If an employee of a facility is injured while acting in the scope of his or her employment, he or she may be entitled to recovery for medical expenses and disability. The health record may be used as evidence before the workers' compensation board to show the severity of the injury and other important medical data.

If the nursing facility receives a court order to produce a record, it must obey the law. Generally, court orders are of two types: (1) a **subpoena**, which is a legal process requiring a witness to appear in court and testify in a particular case, and (2) a **subpoena duces tecum**, which is a legal process requiring a witness with possession of documents important to the issue being tried to come to court with those documents.

COURT APPEARANCES

Appearances in Court with Health Records

Here are guidelines a custodian of health records should follow when appearing in court with a record.

- Obey the court order. It is a legal process and, if ignored, the medical record librarian or the nursing facility may be held in contempt of court.
- Be familiar with the content of the record and make sure it is complete and up to date.
- Be courteous at all times when on the witness stand. Do not make sarcastic or flippant remarks.
- If asked a question that is not understood or to which the answer is unknown, tell the court that this is the case.
- Do not argue with the attorneys and keep calm and cool if they are upsetting on cross-examination.
- Give each response to the best ability, tell the truth, do not hedge on an answer, do not ramble, and answer only the questions asked.
- Consult the facility's attorney if in doubt as how to act on the witness stand.

Court Appearance as a Witness

Here are do's and don'ts for those appearing as witnesses.

- Always appear at a trial neatly dressed and properly groomed. The personal appearance of a witness may influence the judge, jury, and all other parties to the lawsuit.
- Speak clearly and slowly so that the judge, jury, and all other parties in the lawsuit can understand.
- Answer only the questions asked and never contribute additional information if not requested. That information may hurt the party you are appearing for, take up the court's time with irrelevant material, and breach the strict rules of evidence.
- Do not attempt to impress the jury or judge with technical language unless qualified to appear as an expert witness.
- Do not lose your temper and insult the attorneys or judge.
- Do not be sarcastic with the judge or attorneys. Keep in mind that the attorney is qualified as to the admission of evidence and proper conduct of the proceedings.
- Do not ramble and talk about subjects not at issue.

CHAPTER 2

Tort Law

A tort is a legal wrong resulting from a breach of a duty fixed by law for which a person may be liable in damages. It is a private wrong between individuals, in contrast to a crime, which is a public wrong. Liability in tort occurs in one of three ways.

1. **Intentional conduct**—An intentional tort is a legal wrong whereby a person intends to do something to adversely affect the interests of another illegally.
2. **Negligent conduct**—An unintentional tort is negligence or the failure to adhere to a standard of care that a reasonably prudent man would have adhered to under the same or similar conditions.
3. **Liability without fault**—Liability without fault, or strict liability, is imposed by law upon a person or entity without proof of fault and is intentional or unintentional in nature. Some areas where the liability without fault concept is used and the insurer pays for the resulting injury or damage without proof of fault of either party, as provided by state statute, are: workers' compensation, wild animal cases, performance of inherently dangerous acts, and automobile accidents.

INTENTIONAL TORTS

Assault

An assault is a threatening gesture by the defendant to strike the plaintiff or put him or her in fear of being struck, whereby the plaintiff experiences reasonable apprehension. Under certain circumstances, the wrongful use of restraints or siderails may result in a nursing facility employee being held responsible for assaulting a resident. The following elements are necessary to have a completed assault:

- **Threatening gesture**—The gesture must be of a nature where the actions or words by the defendant would reasonably create apprehension or fear in the mind of the plaintiff that he or she will suffer bodily harm.
- **Present intent**—An intent on the part of the defendant to strike the plaintiff or to put him or her in fear of being hurt must be immediate and not sometime in the future. For example, the administrator confronts the director of nurses and says, "Mary, if you don't leave this room within the next three days, I will shoot you dead." There is no assault because the threat and the intent to do bodily harm is at some future (not the present) time.
- **Apparent present ability**—There must be apparent present ability of the defendant to strike an immediate blow. If a person stands 100 yards away from another individual and shouts threats to hit him or her, there is no apparent ability to strike an immediate blow from that distance.
- **Reasonable apprehension**—There must be reasonable apprehension by the plaintiff of being struck and hurt by the defendant. If a 97-pound fragile old lady waves her handkerchief at a 200-pound, 6-foot man and shouts that she is going to severely beat him, there would not be a reasonable fear on the part of the man.

Battery

A battery is a willful and unlawful touching of another without consent. For example, a situation arises where a resident attempts to leave the facility without paying the bill, contrary to the facility's policy that all bills owed by residents must be paid upon discharge. The business manager proceeds to physically restrain the resident from leaving. If such restraint is without doctor's orders and created harm to the resident, the business manager may be legally responsible for committing a battery. To recover for battery, the plaintiff must allege and prove the following elements: an offensive touching or contact resulting in physical injury, lack of consent, and damages.

In the case of *Richmond v. Fisk*, milkman Fisk was told on several occasions by Miss Richmond not to annoy her by presenting the milk bill to her when she was sleeping in the morning. One morning around 5:00 A.M., defendant Fisk walked into Miss Fisk's bedroom and shook her with enough force to wake her up and proceeded to present her with a milk bill. Miss Richmond sued Fisk on the basis of battery. In this case, the court ruled that a battery did take place because of the touching without consent. Said touching being offensive and causing emotional trauma to the plaintiff, damages were awarded to her.

Technical battery is often committed in the area of surgical malpractice. For example, a surgeon obtained a signed consent to remove the patient's gallbladder; while the patient was open, the surgeon proceeded to remove a healthy appendix without the knowledge or consent of the patient. The removal of the appendix under these circumstances is a technical battery, and the surgeon is liable for any resulting harm or damage to the plaintiff relating to the unauthorized removal of the appendix.

False Imprisonment

A false imprisonment is the confinement of a person by force, a reasonable threat of force, or an assertion of legal authority whereby he or she is put in fear of personal harm. For a plaintiff to recover for the tort of false imprisonment, the following elements must be present:

- **Confinement of the plaintiff**—The plaintiff must be placed in a position where he or she is confined and has no reasonable means of escape without fear of bodily harm. If there is a reasonable means of escape and the plaintiff does not take advantage of it, ordinarily there is no false imprisonment.
- **Awareness of confinement**—If a plaintiff is locked in a room while sleeping, there is no false imprisonment because he or she was not conscious of the restraint imposed.
- **Intentional confinement**—The confinement must be an intentional act, not occasioned by error or mistake. A nursing facility administrator may become involved in tort liability for false imprisonment should he or she attempt to physically restrain a resident without legal justification.

Invasion of Privacy

A number of states recognize an individual's inherent right to be protected from communication of information about his or her personal affairs to the public and from the communal use of his or her name. This right is termed the *right of privacy*. The courts have held that the unjustifiable communication of one's private affairs where the public has no legitimate concern is an invasion of that privacy and wrongful interference into private activities.

Invasion of privacy covers four areas.

1. **Taking a person's name or likeness for one's own use or benefit—** For example, without permission, a person uses the name and photograph of a famous football player in an advertisement to sell his product.

2. **Unreasonable intrusion—**Some forms of intrusion include unpermitted entry into a person's home or room in a long-term care facility, an illegal search of a person's property or self, tapping a person's phone without authority, and opening a person's personal mail.

3. **Public disclosure of private facts—**A person is subject to liability for giving publicity to private facts about another that is highly offensive and not a matter of legitimate public concern. The information need not be publicized in the media to be actionable. Persons who have voluntarily become public figures as part of a newsworthy event cannot complain of the publicity of otherwise private facts that are of legitimate public concern.

4. **False light in the public eye—**A person is subject to liability for giving publicity to a matter that places the plaintiff before the public in a false light, providing the false light is highly offensive to a reasonable person and the defendant had knowledge of the falsity of the matter.

Defenses to the Intentional Torts of Assault, Battery, False Imprisonment, and Invasion of Privacy

Defense to a tort action is a justifiable reason on the part of the defendant to legally excuse the action. If an alleged defense prevails, no liability ordinarily occurs on behalf of the defendant. Two defenses to the aforementioned intentional torts are (1) consent by the plaintiff to the alleged tortious act, and (2) self-defense on the part of the defendant. For example, where a patient voluntarily and with full knowledge of the procedures consents to a vaccination by a physician, he or she is not able to recover for an alleged battery because of this consent; where a woman consents and voluntarily submits to an abortion and subsequently sues the physician performing the surgery in a civil suit, she is not able to recover liquidated or money damages because of her consent to the procedure and participation in the crime of abortion, if abortion is illegal in the state.

Defamation

Defamation is the written or oral accusation of an untrue nature against the character of a person that affects his or her reputation in that it holds him or her up to ridicule, contempt, shame, or disgrace among a respectable class of the community. The two broad kinds of defamation are:

1. **Slander** is oral defamation. The elements of slander are:
   * The verbal accusation must discredit the plaintiff.
   * There is an intent to communicate the defamation.
   * A third party must hear the defamatory remark (publication).
   * Damages must be shown.
     Remarks that are slanderous per se do not require that proof of damages be shown. Such remarks are oral imputations:
   * of a punishable offense. For instance, a defendant accuses the administrator of stealing or embezzling funds from the facility.
   * of a loathsome disease. For example, a defendant accuses Mary, an innocent 16-year-old daughter of a renowned minister, of having contracted AIDS because of her immoral activities.
   * in relation to a person's trade, business, or profession. For example, a defendant says at the local medical society meeting, "Dr. Brown, you are the most reckless alcoholic surgeon in our community."
   * of immorality. For instance, a defendant says, "Alice, you are a harlot," when in fact Alice is one of the most virtuous members of the community.
2. **Libel** is a written defamatory communication of an untrue nature to someone other than the person being defamed. The elements of libel are:

- The written words must discredit or impugn the character or reputation of the plaintiff in the eyes of a considerable and respectable class of the community.
- A third party must read the defamatory communication (publication).
- There is intent to communicate the defamatory remark to a third party.
- Damages must be shown.

Defenses to Defamation

There are three defenses to defamation.

1. **Truth**—Truthful information communicated to a third party without malice is a complete defense to the tort of defamation.
2. **Absolute privilege**—Individuals may make remarks that ordinarily would be actionable under certain circumstances where absolute privilege exists. An action in defamation would not be sustained because of absolute privilege in the following situations: a legislator who makes a derogatory remark about another during legislative proceedings, a witness who makes a derogatory remark during a trial or before a duly empowered legislative committee, and an attorney who makes a derogatory statement about the parties during the course of the trial.
3. **Qualified or conditional privilege**—This is a privilege protecting the person who utters or publishes allegedly defamatory material unless he or she has actual malice and knowledge of the falsity of the defamation. This privilege extends to all communications made in good faith upon any subject matter in which the communicating party has an interest or duty to another. For example, a newspaper has a qualified privilege when it fairly and accurately reports the proceedings of a trial, or a former employer has this privilege when making a statement to a new employer regarding the work of an employee. If the person or organization has a qualified privilege, the plaintiff in a defamation action may not recover unless it is proven that there was actual malice on the part of the defendant.

The possible intentional tort of defamation is important to the long-term care facility administrator with regard to disclosure of information to third parties from records or other files without the proper consent of the resident or legal guardian.

UNINTENTIONAL TORTS

Negligence

Negligence is an unintentional tort. It is the doing, or the failure to do, an act that is in violation of a legal duty. It is the failure to act as a reasonably prudent person would have acted under the same conditions or circumstances. Degrees of negligence are classified as slight, ordinary, or gross. However, today the American courts have almost entirely rejected the notion of degrees of negligence as unworkable.

The tort of negligence against a long-term care facility is easy to allege but difficult to prove. It is estimated that 90 percent of negligence cases are settled out of court.

The following four elements are necessary for a cause of action in negligence:

1. **A legal duty owed to the plaintiff**—The general rule is that one is under a duty to all persons at all times to exercise reasonable care for their physical safety and the safety of their property. It is important that the duty owed to the plaintiff is a legal (not merely a moral) duty. For example, two men are standing on the shore of a beach area and, 150 feet away, another man is drowning. One man turns to the other and says, "That man out there is drowning." Is there a legal duty to attempt to save the drowning man? The courts have held that there is no legal duty imposed upon the onlookers. However, if one man decides to take a boat out and rescue the drowning man and negligently hits him with an oar during the attempted rescue, there may be liability imposed on the rescuer. Initially, the man attempting to help had no legal duty to do so, but by helping he assumed a legal duty and an obligation to use reasonable care. The courts have said that even though there is only a moral duty initially, once a legal duty is assumed, it must be pursued in a non-negligent manner.
2. **Breach of that legal duty by the defendant**—The violation of a legal duty can be proved in court by the introduction of evidence showing lack of due care on the part of the defendant. This can be shown by examination of witnesses during a trial and by interrogatories or

dispositions of the parties involved taken under oath prior to the trial to show the following:

- commission of a lawful act done in a careless or negligent manner
- commission of an unlawful act injuring another. This can entail the doctrine of res ipsa loquitor, which applies when the instrumentality that inflicted the injury was subject to the use, inspection, and complete control of the defendant; the act could not have happened except through the negligence of the defendant or his or her agents. Once proven applicable, this doctrine shifts the burden of proof regarding negligence from the plaintiff to the defendant and permits the judge or jury to find negligence without the use of expert testimony.
- failure to perform an act that one is legally bound to do. Does the fact that a defendant violated a statute or ordinance in itself constitute negligence per se? No, such violation is merely evidence of negligence; if the violation is relevant to the issue being litigated, it is admissible as to the consequences the particular statute intended to prevent.

For example, a state has a statute requiring that fire extinguishers be inspected and serviced at least annually in long-term care facilities. A facility has not had the fire extinguishers checked or serviced for two years. A resident trips over the front doorsill and injures herself; she sues the facility for negligence. May the fact that the facility violated the statute regarding the inspection and servicing of fire extinguishers be introduced into evidence in this law action? No, because it is irrelevant to the issue (tripping over the doorsill) of negligence. On the other hand, suppose a fire breaks out in one of the rooms and the resident reaches for a fire extinguisher that fails to work properly, resulting in severe burns to the resident. The facility is sued for negligence. May evidence concerning the violation of the statute be introduced into the case? Yes, the injury that occurred was the result of a direct violation of the statute, which was designed to protect persons from such injury.

3. **A direct or causal connection between the defendant's alleged conduct and the damage suffered by the plaintiff**—This allegation is difficult to prove because it requires testimony and evidence to show that the plaintiff was injured through a direct cause, occurrence, or act initiated by the defendant. The causation must be direct and proximate. A direct causation is when injury to the plaintiff was a

direct result of the defendant's unlawful act; a proximate causation is when the defendant knew, or should have known, the consequences of a particular act, and that these consequences would probably happen as a result of his or her act.

4. **Actual loss or damage to the plaintiff of a recognized kind**—It is necessary that a complaint for negligence allege injury or damages to the plaintiff. Ordinarily, the damages are enunciated and may include physical injury, distress, mental anguish, pain, and suffering. The plaintiff may recover out-of-pocket or compensatory liquidated damages. If the acts of the defendant are found to be willful, wanton, and reckless misconduct, the plaintiff may also recover punitive damages (punishment to the defendant for his or her wrongdoing).

Defenses to Negligence

Defenses to negligence are termed *affirmative defenses*. To be effective, they must be alleged in the answer by the defendant and proven during the trial. As with res ipsa loquitor, affirmative defenses shift the burden of proof from the plaintiff to the defendant. If these defenses are not properly pleaded in the answer, the courts consider them waived. The commonly interposed affirmative defenses are:

- **Contributory negligence**—It is a basic principle of law that if the plaintiff contributes in any way to his or her own injury, he or she cannot recover resulting damages. In some states, the doctrine of comparative negligence applies instead of contributory negligence, where the plaintiff may recover even though he or she was partially negligent for his or her own injury. Usually there is a determination of the percentage of the plaintiff's negligence; that percentage is subtracted from any judgment given in favor of the plaintiff.
- **Assumption of risk**—When a plaintiff consents to assume risk of injury, it is said to be a complete defense. This doctrine is predicated upon the fact that the plaintiff was aware of the risk involved and exposed him- or herself to the particular hazard anyway.
- **Accord and satisfaction**—This means that the parties to a lawsuit have come to an amicable compromise to settle the suit between themselves for a stipulated amount. Both parties are satisfied and agree to dismiss the action.

- **Statutes of limitations**—These are periods during which a tort action can be filed after an injury occurs. If legal action is not brought within the required period of time and such defense is properly treated in the answer, the plaintiff cannot bring the action. A statute of limitations begins to run on the date where a single injury is caused by a single event (for example, professional malpractice) whether or not the plaintiff knows his or her injury was caused by a wrongful act.

  A statute of limitations may be tabled and not run in several instances. If the injury is not capable of being readily seen, a special rule (the discovery rule) may be applicable. Decisions or statutes of a particular state may provide that a cause of action does not accrue until the plaintiff becomes aware of the wrongful act. (For example, assume that a two-year statute of limitations exists for a professional malpractice action and that a surgical instrument was left in a patient's body. The patient/plaintiff may experience symptoms but has no reason to expect that the symptoms are the result of the surgeon's wrongful act. By the time the plaintiff discovers the wrong, it is more than two years after the surgery. The plaintiff can bring a lawsuit for resulting injuries within two years of discovering the surgeon's wrongful act.) A statute of limitations is also tabled when a plaintiff is a minor or mentally incompetent, or when the defendant has fraudulently concealed facts from which the plaintiff could have determined that he or she has a cause of action.

- **Statutes of repose**—Unlike statutes of limitations, these statutes start to run when the harmful act is complete whether or not there is an injury, allowing a plaintiff's claim to be barred before a cause of action arises. The purpose of these statutes is to eliminate the possibility of claims arising many years after a wrongful act. These statutes have become common in recent years and are limited to medical or other professional negligence claims. Most statutes of repose have been upheld against constitutional challenges.

CHAPTER 3

Law of Contracts

A contract is a promise or set of promises to which the law attaches a legal obligation. It involves two or more parties and is legally binding to all. A contract is a basic tool ensuring that desires and promises are carried out and obligations met. This legal instrument documents a meeting of the minds of the parties to the contract as to the items and actions involved.

REQUIREMENTS FOR VALID CONTRACTS

Certain requirements must be met for a contract to be valid and enforceable by law. These are mutual assent of the parties, a legal agreement, valid consideration, and capacity of the parties to contract.

Mutual Assent of the Parties

Mutual assent of the parties takes the form of an offer by one party and an acceptance by the other party. The offer is an expression of present intent to enter into a contract that is definite, certain, and properly communicated to the other party. The acceptance is the agreement by the other party to the terms of the offer with the intent to accept the offer; a valid acceptance must be absolute and meet the conditions of the offer. For example:

The Prairiewood Medical Supply Company sends an advertisement that reads, "I have a supply of new hi-lo beds that I will sell for $150 each." An administrator sends a check for $150, ordering a bed; the check is returned.

Is there a valid contract? No. The supply company advertisement is merely an invitation to do business, not an offer. The sending of the money and order is the offer; the return of the check is a refusal to accept the offer.

Legality of the Agreement

The formation and the performance of the contract must be legal. The law will not aid any of the parties to an illegal agreement, making it unenforceable. Criminal contracts and contracts contrary to public policy are not considered legal.

If the contract is *illegal on its face*, it is unenforceable by either party. For example:

Nursing Facilities X, Y, and Z are the only facilities in a particular community; there are no other facilities within 100 miles in the area. The administrators of X, Y, and Z get together and execute an agreement in writing that room rates in the three facilities will be $100 per day regardless of cost and income. X violates the written agreement and charges $75 per day; Y sues X for breach of the contract.

May Nursing Facility Y recover? No. This agreement is illegal on its face, because it is in restraint of trade, tending to create a monopoly and is, therefore, unenforceable by all parties to it.

If the contract tends to *impose unreasonable hardship* upon a person, it is considered illegal and against public policy. For example:

The Piety Nursing Facility is one of a chain of profit-making facilities located all over the country. The central office enters into an agreement with an applicant to become administrator of the Piety Nursing Facility. This facility enters into an agreement with the administrator that provides that if he leaves the Piety Nursing Facility voluntarily or for cause, he will not accept employment in another facility within 100 miles for three years from the date of severance. After six months, the administrator quits his job and accepts employment in a nursing facility 20 miles away. The Piety Nursing Facility sues him for breach of contract.

May the nursing facility recover? No. This contract imposes upon the administrator an undue hardship that is out of proportion against the competition (as was sought by the Piety Nursing Facility). It is, therefore, illegal and unenforceable by the Piety Nursing Facility.

If the contract *violates a public or private fiduciary duty*, it is also illegal and unenforceable. For example:

> The Sunset Valley Nursing Facility has a large financial interest in seeing that certain tax measures are passed by the legislature. The facility hires Attorney X and promises to pay him $10,000 to draw up the required bill, present it to the proper committee, and appear to present strong arguments in favor of the bill. Actually, the bill is in the public interest if passed. The attorney does all the work regarding the bill; the Sunset Valley Nursing Facility refuses to pay him. The attorney sues the facility.
>
> May he recover? No. Review of the contract says that this is an illegal contract. The illegality involves not the drawing up of the bill or the argument for its passage; the attempt to influence the voting on the bill for money was held to be against public policy. It is considered the duty of citizens to do such things for the public interest without pay.

Valid Consideration

For a contract to be valid and enforceable, it must be supported by valid consideration. Consideration is defined as "a legal benefit received by the person making a promise or a legal detriment suffered by the person to whom the promise has been made." In other words, each party must give up something of value. Such acts as payment of money or doing something that one is not legally bound to do are said to be good consideration. The consideration is usually recited in a written contract.

Capacity of the Parties to Contract

Both parties to the contract must have the necessary contractual capacity to form a valid and enforceable contract. Generally, each party must be of sound mind and legal age. Otherwise, the contract may be classified as void or voidable.

TYPES OF CONTRACTS

A **formal contract** is required by law to be in writing if it is to be valid. These contracts are usually deeds, mortgages, or other instruments under seal. The statute of frauds in each state specifies what kinds of contracts must be in writing.

A **simple contract** is not required to be in writing and may be oral.

An **express contract** is actual written or oral agreement of the parties to its terms that is openly uttered or declared at the time of making it, in distinct and explicit language. For example:

> A nursing home administrator orally offers to buy a package of catheters at a certain price. The salesman orally accepts the offer. This is an express binding oral contract.

An **implied contract** manifests the terms by actions and is well understood by the parties without being specifically written. These contracts are divided into two classes: contracts implied in fact and contracts implied in law.

- *A contract implied in fact* is one established by the conduct of the parties rather than by their express declarations. For example:

> John Jones goes to the local restaurant and orders dinner. The waitress serves it to him. After consuming the dinner, he pays for it. A contractual relationship exists here. The ordering of the meal consists of an offer; the serving of the meal indicates acceptance of this offer.

- *A contract implied in law* is imposed upon a person by the law irrespective of the intent to enter into a contract. It is not created by mutual assent of the parties. For example:

> A truck with the name of a painting firm drives up to a nursing facility. The painter gets out and starts painting the outside of the facility. The administrator watches him do the job and keeps silent. A week later the firm sends a bill for $200 for painting services. There was no express offer made by the administrator; there was no mutual assent. Due to the fact that the administrator remained silent, the law says that the facility is obligated to pay for the paint job.

Thus, the distinction between a contract implied in fact and a contract implied in law is that the contract implied in fact is one in which the act or conduct infers an agreement and the contract implied in law imposes a duty by law so that one party will not be unjustly enriched.

A **void contract** imposes no liability whatsoever on the party making the contract if he or she does not have the contractual capacity. For example:

> Mary Jones, a 93-year-old senile woman judicially declared incompetent, promises to pay $500 for an escort to the art festival in town. The escort performs his part of the contract and then asks for the money. She refuses to pay.
>
> May the escort collect for breach of contract? No. The promise to pay the money is completely void because Mary has been judicially declared to be incompetent and, therefore, does not have the legal capacity to enter into a valid contract.

A **voidable contract** is valid and enforceable unless it is legally disaffirmed by the party having the right to avoid the contract. For example:

> John Jones, a 16-year-old minor, buys a new Oldsmobile from Happy Joe on a conditional sales agreement. At the time of the agreement, John stated that he is 25 years old. The contract is for $5,800, of which John pays $200 down. The very next day John drives the car into the side of the local nursing facility, ruining the car. John calls Happy Joe, tells him of the accident, and directs him to tow the car to his garage. The remains of the car are towed away. Then John says, "Guess what, I'm only 16 years old, and I disaffirm the contract." Happy Joe then sues John for breach of the conditional sales contract.
>
> May he recover? No. The general rule is that an infant or minor may disaffirm his or her contract and plead infancy. The law allows this protection for minors in order to shield them from sharp or unethical operators during the so-called years of inexperience.

A **unilateral contract** is one in which the consideration for the contract is an act on the part of one of the parties in return for a promise by the other.

A **bilateral contract** is one in which the consideration is a promise by one party and a return promise by the other party.

LIFE CARE CONTRACTS

The life care contract takes form when a resident or applicant for admission to the nursing facility agrees to pay a stipulated amount as an entrance fee and/or to transfer all present and after acquired property to the facility in consideration for the facility rendering care to the resident for the rest of his or her life. Generally, the courts interpret the life care contract the same as any other type of legal contract. However, some of these contracts have been questioned concerning their validity and enforceability on legal issues involving lack of mutuality, insufficient consideration, illegality, unconscionable contract, death before the effective date, and death during the probationary period. The following cases discuss some of these issues.

Lack of Assent or Mutuality

In the following case, the contract between the facility and the resident was attacked on the grounds that no absolute mutual obligations existed. The contract between facility and resident must require continuing performance of the obligations between the parties to indicate mutuality and be enforceable.

> In the case of *Henry Keep Home v. Moore et al.*, 176 P 2d 1016, a contract was entered into between the plaintiff, a charitable corporate nursing facility with a bed capacity of about 35 residents, and Mrs. P. The nursing facility had a rule that to be admitted, the applicant must agree to convey to the facility all real and personal property. When Mrs. P made application to the facility, this rule was explained to her. She was 80 years old and said she was in good health. The application form was fully explained to her beforehand; part of the application agreement read, "Having passed the required physical and mental examination for admission, I am aware of the facts that the admission fee of $1,000 is to be paid in advance and that all my real and personal property is to be given absolutely to the home." Mrs. P's application was accepted by the facility; she remained there as a resident for about three years until her death. During this period, the facility paid for her living expenses, provided her with nursing, hospital, and medical care, and paid for her burial. One of the properties owned by the resident had not been turned over to the facility by deed. This action by the facility requested that the estate specifically perform that part of the contract made by the decedent.
>
> The court held that the facility had carried out its part of the contractual agreement to care for the resident during the remainder of her life and, therefore, was entitled to have the land in question transferred to it. The court stated that in this case, the contract was definite and mutual and, therefore, binding.

Sufficiency of Consideration

Some life care contracts have been attacked on the basis of insufficient consideration. Most of the cases have held that in a life care contract where a resident transfers his or her property to the nursing facility, that property is sufficient consideration for the contract.

In the case of *Wilson v. Dexter*, 192 NE 2d 469, the issue of insufficiency of consideration by the nursing facility was raised in an effort to defeat the life care contract. The resident agreed to turn over most of her property in return for lifetime care in an apartment operated by the nursing facility. The resident lived only 42 days after she entered the facility and was in the hospital section during the entire time. The major contention of the beneficiaries under her will was that the consideration for the contract failed and the estate of the decedent should go to them, not to the nursing facility under the duly executed life care contract. It was argued that the contract provided for a room in a certain building and that the resident had never entered that specific room. There was evidence in the case pointing out that the nursing facility did prepare a special room for the resident in the stipulated building. The room had remained available for her use, even though she was confined to a bed in the hospital section of the nursing facility.

The court held that the nursing facility performed its obligation under the contract; therefore, the consideration was sufficient and the funds went to the nursing facility.

The other issue raised in the case concerned the relative value of consideration given by the nursing facility. The defendant claimed that while the resident did not receive over $1,000 worth of services, the nursing facility was to receive over $20,000 from the plaintiff.

As to this issue, the court said, "It is true that the home received substantially more from the contract than it gave; nevertheless, the consideration that the home was contractually obligated to give in service by the life care contract was an indeterminable amount that could have ranged from that which was actually given to an amount exceeding $20,000." The court went on to say that the important factor is that the facility was *ready* to perform those services for the remainder of the resident's life. The facility had adequately performed its part of the contract and was entitled to full payment by the estate of the resident.

Unfair Contracts

Life care contracts have also been said to be invalid where the contract is said to be unfair to one of the parties.

Even though a nursing facility may obtain money out of proportion to its services, the reason why such life care contracts are upheld is well stated by the court in *Fidelity Union Trust Company v. Reeves*, 129 A 922, saying, "The public welfare is better served by upholding contracts of this kind whereby institutions which are for the aged and tend to relieve the public of their charge are facilitated in their work for the poor, than to put the ban of law on them because perchance some of the unfortunates might quite accidentally be favored by the death of a rich relative or friend, and to them the services of a home in their declining years far outweighs the advent of such a remote possibility."

In *Stiegelmeier v. West Side Deutscher Fraun Verun*, 178 NE 2d 516, the resident, upon admission, turned over to the nursing facility all of his assets, amounting to $6,000. In consideration for the money, the facility agreed to provide the resident for the remainder of his life with living quarters, food, clothing, and medical and nursing care as needed and, upon his death, a proper burial. Less than one and a half years later, the resident was admitted to a state hospital. The issue arose as to whether the fact that the nursing facility got the $6,000 for almost one and a half years of service to the resident constituted an unjust or unconscionable contract.

The court held that this contractual agreement was not unconscionable or against public policy.

Fraud or Undue Influence

The question of fraud or undue influence has been discussed in connection with some life care contracts.

In *General German Aged Peoples Home v. Hammerbacker*, 3 A 678, 54 Amer Rep 782, a resident wishing to be admitted to the nursing facility was required to pay a stipulated admitting fee and to transfer all of his property or income of any kind to the facility. The resident asserted in writing that he only had $300 in property. He was then accepted into the facility without any conveyance of his property and remained there until he died. After his death, it was learned that at the time of his admission, he did have property worth $1,200.

The court held that the decedent had perpetuated a fraud upon the institution in securing his admission without a legal conveyance of his property.

In *Old Men's Home v. Lee Estate*, 4 S 2d 235, an issue arose as to whether a nursing facility should be reimbursed for services it rendered in absence of an express contractual agreement. Here an aged and sickly man was admitted to the nursing facility on the basis that he was poor, whereas in fact at the time of his admission to the facility and up until his death, he had assets of about $5,000. There was no express agreement signed by the nursing facility or the resident at the time of admission.

The court in this case said that the facility was entitled to reimbursement for the care and services it rendered upon the basis of a quasi-contract or a legal contract based upon the principle that a person shall not be unjustly enriched at the expense of another.

Death of a Resident during the Probationary Period

Some life care contracts provide for a probationary period whereby either party may dissolve that agreement without cause. In the event that the resident voluntarily leaves or the facility refuses to admit him or her as a permanent resident at the end of the probationary period, usually all payments made to the facility, less the cost of any services provided, are refunded to the resident.

What happens if the applicant dies during this probationary period without being accepted or rejected as a permanent resident of the facility? May the facility keep the property of the resident on the grounds that the agreement has not been dissolved or must it return the property to the decedent's estate?

First National Bank v. Methodist Home for the Aged, 309 P 2d 389, addressed these issues. The nursing facility prepared a life care contract that provided that the prospective resident pay a stipulated cash amount for admission to the facility; the contract provided for a two-month probationary period with the right of either party to determine whether the resident would stay in the facility at the end of the probation. The resident died during the probationary period, and the question arose as to whether the nursing facility could legally keep the fee.

The court held that the nursing facility must return the fee less any amount accumulated for maintenance of the resident during the probationary period.

The wording of some life care contracts is not clear. It is important that both parties fully understand the agreement they are executing.

In *Ferrand v. Redington Memorial Home*, 270 A 2d 871, the nursing facility prepared a life care contract that provided that if the resident were still residing there at the time of his death, the facility would pay expenses of sickness and funeral; all assets turned over to the institution by the resident would remain the property of the nursing facility. The resident died during the probationary period, and the issue arose as to whether the facility could enforce the agreement.

The court held that the life care contract was ambiguous as to whether the assets should be returned to the administrator of the decedent's estate. The court stated that the term *resides* ordinarily connotes more than a transient location and that because the contract was drawn up by the nursing facility, any ambiguity would be construed in favor of the administrator of the estate.

Transfer to a Hospital

Who receives the assets if a resident is transferred to a hospital when he or she is under a life care contract? Whether or not the assets left to the facility under the terms of the life care contract are legally the property of the resident or nursing facility depends upon the fact situation when the resident is transferred to a hospital before his or her death.

In *Connelly v. Methodist Home of the District of Columbia*, 190 A 2d 550, an admission agreement was executed whereby the resident assigned all legacies, funds, and credits she possessed or would possess to the nursing facility in consideration for being admitted. After 14 months in the facility, she became emotionally unstable and was transferred to a psychiatric facility. The guardian or committee of the resident at the psychiatric hospital attempted to recover the proceeds of an endowment policy that had matured and been paid by the insurance company to the nursing facility pursuant to the life care contract.

The court held that the psychiatric facility could not recover the money.

A somewhat contrary outcome resulted in *Chappell v. Odd Fellows Home*, 136 A 2d 72, where the resident executed a life care contract with the nursing facility at the time of admission. During the resident's stay, she became overactive and noisy and was not able to adjust to the nursing facility environment. She was transferred to a mental hospital when the facility's board of trustees said she could no longer stay there. While at the psychiatric hospital, the resident died; the administratrix of her estate attempted to recover the property that the resident had conveyed to the nursing facility pursuant to the life care contract.

The court held that the administratrix was entitled to recover the property because the nursing facility's admission rules state that a resident's property may be returned if the board of trustees decides that the best interests of the facility require that the resident leave. The court did allow the facility to recover an amount for maintenance and board in accordance with its rules and regulations.

Death before Effective Date

What is the effect of the death of a resident before the effective date of a life care contract?

The case of *Gold v. Salem Lutheran Association*, 347 P 2d 687, discussed this issue. An 84-year-old male resident executed a life care contract in consideration for the promise by the nursing facility to provide for food, lodging, and care for the remainder of his life. The resident died before the performance of the contract was to start, and the estate attempted to cancel or rescind the contract on the basis of failure of consideration on the part of the nursing facility.

The court held that the contract was not subject to cancellation; the estate could not recover an amount already paid to the facility because the promise by the nursing facility to provide services to the resident was sufficient consideration to the agreement.

NURSING FACILITY ADMINISTRATOR'S EMPLOYMENT CONTRACT

The field of long-term care administration is a profession due to licensure statutes and the upgrading of standards in nursing facilities. The nursing home administrator, as the chief executive of the facility, should have the protection of an employment contract executed by the administrator and the nursing facility. The term of the contract should be for two or three years, with an option to renew at the end of the employment period. Here is a sample contract, which may be used as a guide.

AGREEMENT

WHEREAS, the __(Name of Facility)__, a corporation (partnership, sole proprietorship) of __(City)__, __(State)__, hereinafter called the Nursing Facility, and __(Name of Administrator)__, hereinafter called Administrator, agree to enter into an employment contract.

NOW THEREFORE, in consideration of mutual covenants, promises, and provisions of this agreement, it is hereby agreed by and between the Nursing Facility and Administrator that:

I

The Nursing Facility hereby employs ___(Name of Administrator)___ as the Administrator of the ___(Nursing Facility)___.

II

Duties

(If the duties of the administrator are not included in the employment contract, they should be outlined in the constitution and bylaws of the corporation or in some other written document.)

1. The Administrator shall exercise general management of the Nursing Facility.
2. The Administrator shall provide for the implementation of policies, directives, and resolutions promulgated by the ownership.
3. The Administrator shall see to it that the rules and regulations of the State Board of Health and the recommendations of approving and other regulatory agencies are complied with regarding the operation of the Facility.
4. The Administrator shall develop, maintain, and administer a sound plan of organization.
5. The Administrator shall be responsible for seeing that high standards of resident care are maintained.
6. The Administrator shall maintain the Nursing Facility in a solvent condition and make such recommendations to the ownership as are necessary to the attainment of this objective.
7. The Administrator is responsible for the supervision of the preparation of the annual budget.
8. Regarding capital expenditures, the Administrator must present to the ownership requests for new and replacement equipment not included in the annual budget for any amount over $_____.
9. The Administrator shall obtain approval from the ownership for:
   a. Plans and procedures involving major structural changes of the physical plant.
   b. Major changes in personnel policies and wage and salary programs.
   c. Plans and new policies expanding or deleting health services.
   d. Major changes in rates and charges for services.
   e. Initial contractual agreements regarding third-party payers such as Medicare, Medicaid, and welfare.
   f. Creation of any new positions, new department, or new educational programs.
10. The Administrator shall develop a working relationship with third-party payers.

11. The Administrator shall cooperate with other health care facilities so that the health needs of the community are coordinated.
12. The Administrator shall develop and maintain a favorable image of the Nursing Facility by keeping the public informed and cooperating with the news media.
13. The Administrator shall report regularly to the ownership and submit an annual report on the operation of the Nursing Facility.
14. The following may be added for administrators of facilities with an organized medical staff:
    a. The Administrator shall present to the ownership recommendations for staff appointments, reappointments, and conferring of privileges as made by the executive committee of the medical staff.
    b. The Administrator shall assist the medical staff in revising staff bylaws.
    c. The Administrator shall present to the governing body resignation of a medical staff member or request for curtailment of staff privileges as recommended by the medical staff.
    d. The Administrator shall present to the governing body contractual agreements with staff specialists for approval.
15. The Administrator shall perform the aforementioned duties and others that may be assigned to him or her by the governing body to the best of his or her ability.

III

The Nursing Facility agrees to pay the Administrator a salary of $_____ per annum effective ___(Date)___.

IV

The Nursing Facility shall give the Administrator an annual vacation of _____.

V

The Administrator shall be subject to the policies of the Nursing Facility as may be established from time to time respecting sick leave, paid holidays, and reimbursement for travel expenses.

VI

This agreement shall remain in full force and effect for a term of ____ years from and after ___(Date)___ provided, however, that either the Nursing Facility or the Administrator shall have the right and privilege of canceling and terminating this agreement.

VII

It is agreed that this contract may be terminated for due cause by either party thereto on 90 days written notice clearly outlining the cause of such termination to the other, said notice to be sent by registered mail to the address of the other party.

VIII

The parties to this employment contract may appeal any terms regarding termination for due cause to a court of competent jurisdiction within the state said contract was executed.

IN WITNESS WHEREOF, the Nursing Facility and the Administrator have caused this Agreement to be duly and properly executed at ___(City)___ , ___(State)___ , this ____ day of ___(Month)___ , ___.

_____
Administrator

_____
Nursing Facility

_____
Witness

_____
Witness

CHAPTER 4

Vicarious Liability

Vicarious liability, or respondeat superior, is a form of strict liability by which an employer is liable, in certain instances, for the wrongful acts of employees.

Respondeat superior is based upon the premise that the "master should respond or reply" for the negligent acts of his or her servants or employees and upon the principles of agency law; the employee is said to be acting for and on behalf of the employer. From a practical viewpoint, the courts have indicated that the funds for the payment of a judgment are most likely to be in the ownership. The respondeat superior theory transfers the liability from the negligent employee to the ownership. This theory, if applied to the nursing facility operation, makes the ownership (whether it be a proprietorship, partnership, or corporation) ultimately liable for the negligent acts of its employees or agents. Before the court will apply this theory, two criteria must be established. There must be a showing in law that an employer-employee relationship exists and that the employee's alleged negligent acts were performed within the scope of his or her employment.

If a nursing facility must pay a judgment because of the negligence of an employee, the facility does have the right to indemnification. This means that the facility may sue the negligent employee to recover the amount it was forced to pay because of the theory of respondeat superior. From a practical viewpoint, however, a recovery from the employee rarely is accomplished inasmuch as most employees are judgment-proof due to a lack of assets. If the employee is a professional nurse and is covered by professional liability insurance, the employer may bring an action against the insurance company for the purpose of recovering any money paid as a result of the nurse's negligent acts under the theory of respondeat superior.

A jury or other trier of fact determines if a nurse is an employee of the nursing facility and acting within the scope of his or her employment for the purpose of vicarious liability. Whether the relationship was that of employer-employee or of independent contractor is generally determined by the fact that the nursing facility did have control or the right to control the person in performance of his or her duties. An independent contractor is one who becomes legally and ultimately responsible for his or her own negligent acts. If the nursing facility does not have the requisite direction and control of the acts of the person committing the alleged negligent act, the relationship may well be one of independent contractor. In a nursing facility situation, the consulting physician, the attending physician, the private-duty nurse, and other professional consultants, depending upon their contractual relationship with the facility, may be deemed to be independent contractors.

The test to determine whether or not a person is acting within the scope of his or her employment is whether or not that individual is doing an act that is proximately related to what he or she was hired to do. A number of cases have held that a health care facility is not responsible if an employee was "on a frolic of his or her own" rather than carrying out the duties mandated by his or her employer.

Although liability may be imposed on a facility by the negligent acts of any employee acting within the scope of his or her employment, many of the employees involved in vicarious liability are nursing personnel. Because of the varying relationships between nursing personnel and the nursing facility, physicians, and residents and the varying scopes of employment, it is important to differentiate among the types of nursing personnel working in long-term care facilities.

- A **registered nurse** (RN) has graduated from an accredited school of nursing and licensed to practice within the state where he or she holds the license. He or she has attended a four-year degree program affiliated with a university, a three-year degree program connected with a hospital, or a two-year associate degree program connected with a community college. An RN practices in a variety of areas (general duty, industrial, operating room, nurse anesthetist) in hospitals and long-term care facilities. The field of geriatric nursing is a specialized type of nursing; nurses working in the nursing facility environment must be familiar with phases of medicine and nursing with which an acute hospital nurse may not be familiar.

- A **licensed practical nurse** (LPN) or certified vocational nurse (CVN) has graduated from a practical school of nursing and is licensed to practice within his or her state.
- A **nurse aide/assistant** or certified nurse aide (CNA) has completed 75-hour mandatory training and has passed a competency evaluation program within four months of employment. A high school diploma or previous experience is not required. Aides completing the program are placed on the state registry for nurse aides.

While the educational backgrounds of the levels of nursing personnel differ considerably, another basic difference in their functions or scopes of employment in a long-term care facility is in the latitude of making nursing judgments for the care of the resident.

- **Registered nurses** must act in a manner consistent with their training and background under the general direction and supervision of a duly qualified physician. They are responsible for assessment, planning, implementation, and evaluation of resident care and must use good nursing judgment in the performance of these duties. They delegate to LPNs and CVNs and carry a primary obligation to supervise the nursing personnel. They are responsible for the majority of high-level treatments and must be aware of the latest techniques. Professional nurses must be familiar with the use, dosage, potential hazards, and manner of administration of medications. They observe and accurately record all important data relating to the care of the resident.

  The number of RNs employed by a facility has a direct relationship to the level of care rendered by that facility. To be licensed and to participate in federal programs, both nursing facilities (NFs) and skilled nursing facilities (SNFs) are required by federal and state law to have a certain number of professional nurses on staff. The NF is not required to employ as many professional nurses as the SNF and may employ a larger number of LPNs.

- **Licensed practical nurses** and certified vocational nurses care for the sick, injured, convalescing, and handicapped under the direction of physicians and registered nurses. Most LPNs and CVNs provide basic bedside care: take vital signs, assist with activities of daily living (ADLs), treat bedsores, give injections, insert catheters, administer prescribed medication (where state law permits), etc. Observations and adverse reactions to medications and treatments are reported to the registered nurses. LPNs and CVNs are often charge nurses in long-term care facilities and help to evaluate resident needs, develop care plans, and supervise nurse aides.

- **Nurse aides** assist the RNs and LPNs by providing specific routine care to long-term care residents: handling personal care (bathing, feeding, and grooming), taking and recording temperatures and pulse rates, measuring fluid intake and output, answering the call system, and performing other specific duties not requiring nursing judgment. Aides must report observations to the professional nurses in charge.

- **Private-duty nurses** have a different legal status altogether because they are considered an independent contractor and negligent acts are a personal responsibility and not imputed to the facility. These nurses are usually hired directly by the resident and are, therefore, generally considered an employee of the resident. However, some courts feel that health care facilities may hide behind the independent contractor theory in order to avoid responsibility for the care of residents by private-duty nurses.

> In a Missouri case, the court emphasized the fact that a patient had requested a private-duty nurse directly from the hospital. Because the hospital had selected the nurse and was paid for her services, the court found that the private-duty nurse was an agent of the hospital. Damages resulting when the patient jumped out of the window and was injured due to this nurse's negligence were imputed to the hospital.

Another theory important to determining the negligence of nurses working in the nursing facility is the "borrowed servant" theory. This theory states that, under certain conditions, a nurse's negligence, instead of being imputed to the facility, could be imputed to the physician under whose direction and control the nurse is working. Under these conditions, the nurse becomes the employee of the doctor and not of the nursing facility; the physician is then liable for the nurse's negligent acts under respondeat superior. The fact that a resident's attending physician aids the nurse in a nursing facility to perform some act for his or her patient does not make the nurse automatically the physician's employee instead of the nursing facility's employee. The alleged negligent act performed by the nurse is important in the determination of liability. The general rule is that routine acts ordered by the physician and performed by a nurse are considered the nurse's customary duty as an employee of the nursing facility, not as an employee of the physician. However, where the facility surrenders the direction and control of the acts of the nurse to the physician, it is no longer held liable for his or her nonroutine negligent acts under respondeat superior.

LIABILITY OF NURSING PERSONNEL AND OTHER EMPLOYEES

State laws and the Code of Federal Regulations (42 CFR, Part 430 to end) regulate the provision of care in long-term care facilities to ensure that residents receive the necessary services to maintain or attain high practicable physical, mental, and psychosocial well-being in an environment that promotes quality of life for each resident. The following cases cover some areas where the nursing facility may be held liable for damages caused by its employees' negligence under respondeat superior and vicarious liability.

This case involves the failure of nurses and nurse assistants to supervise resident care by not responding to call lights in a timely manner. In *Russell on Behalf of Wunstell v. Kossover*, 634 So 2d 72, Mrs. Wunstell, the mother of the plaintiff, was a diabetic with a history of excessive tobacco use who also suffered from arthrosclerosis, angina, and organic brain syndrome. In April 1987, she was admitted to Norman Health Care Center in acute danger of death. Her doctor prescribed insulin, pain medications, and other drugs, which were administered to her with the warning not to try to move without assistance from nursing personnel. Restraints were suggested but refused by Mrs. Wunstell. Mrs. Wunstell had gotten dizzy and fallen as an effect of the medication. The nursing facility was advised that during a previous stay at a hospital, she had fallen three times.

On May 3, 1987, Nurse Graves gave Mrs. Wunstell her prescribed dosage of Librium. Mrs. Wunstell was discovered on the floor of her room suffering from a broken hip about 20 minutes later. She was taken to Tulane Medical Center. Because of her serious preexisting medical conditions, a hip fixation could not be done immediately, and she was given pain medication. On May 9, 1987, Mrs. Wunstell died due to cardiac arrest.

At the trial, there was considerable testimony that the facility nursing personnel did not respond in a timely manner to the call button in Mrs. Wunstell's room. The call button was placed in a inconvenient position out of the resident's reach. When her daughter pushed the button, there was no timely response by any nurse or nurse assistant employed by the facility. Ample testimony supported the fact that the facility personnel had a history of failing to reply to her calls in a timely manner.

The court concluded that the nursing personnel had breached the standard of care owed to Mrs. Wunstell and awarded damages of $46,000 to the daughter for the pain, suffering, and mental anguish suffered by Mrs. Wunstell. Because of the actions of its nurses and nurse assistants, the facility had to pay the damages under the respondeat superior and vicarious liability rules.

This case points out that a facility may be held liable for damages if an LPN in its employ fails to see that residents are cared for and protected by failing to supervise nurse assistants. In *Hicks v. Department of Health*, 570 NYS 2d 395, Frances S. Hicks, a licensed practical nurse, was employed by the Daughters of Sarah Nursing Facility. Her duties included shift supervision of the facility's nurse assistants to see that they had completed their assignments in providing direct care to the residents. Mrs. Hicks was required to conduct walking rounds at the end of her shift to see that the residents were getting proper attention.

The nurse's record for August 1, 1987, indicated that a security guard found a resident, "H.C.," that evening lying in the dark, half in his bed and half restrained in an overturned wheelchair. "H.C." was in his undershirt with his briefs partially off; his pants, shirt, and socks were on the floor near the door. He was covered with urine and stool, which had hardened and dried on his skin.

After a hearing, an administrative law judge confirmed neglect and assessed a penalty to be paid by both the facility and the negligent LPN. Mrs. Hicks appealed the administrative law judge's findings.

The New York Court of Appeals upheld the administrative law judge and said that the LPN was responsible for ensuring that the nurse assistants' tasks were properly accomplished by conducting a visual check of each resident while making rounds at the end of her shift. Sufficient evidence had been introduced to show that she had not made proper rounds to observe that "H.C." was not in bed and safe.

Negligent treatment must be reported by nurses or therapists to their superiors. In *Poor Sisters of St. Francis v. Catron*, 435 NE 2d 305, Sharon

Catron was brought to the hospital emergency room at 3:40 A.M. on September 12, 1970, in a coma, a result of a drug overdose. The emergency room doctor on duty, Dr. Knochel, inserted an endotracheal tube to help her breathing. Ms. Catron was admitted to the intensive care unit (ICU) of the hospital under the care of her family physician, Dr. Ralph Weller.

Five days later, the family physician ordered a nurse to remove the tube. When the nurse was unable to do so, Dr. Weller did it. Later that day, when Ms. Catron began having difficulty breathing, Dr. Weller ordered a tracheostomy. Ms. Catron's condition improved; she was discharged from the hospital on September 23, 1970. After release, Ms. Catron experienced more breathing difficulties, requiring that she go back to the hospital for another tracheostomy. She also experienced difficulty speaking and underwent several operations to remove scar tissue and open the voice box. The operations were unsuccessful. Ms. Catron sued Dr. Knochel and the hospital for the negligent injury of her throat, vocal cords, and voice box by the endotracheal tube. At the time of the trial, she could not speak above a whisper.

The trial court found that the hospital was liable for the negligent actions of the nurses and therapist and that there was lack of actionable negligence by Dr. Knochel. The jury rendered a verdict of $150,000 against the hospital.

The Court of Appeals of Indiana said that the record in this case showed that nurses who work in ICUs and inhalation therapists are specially trained to handle patients who have endotracheal tubes inserted. Testimony showed that, as a general rule, endotracheal tubes should not be left in a patient longer than three or four days. Both the head nurse and the inhalation therapist at the hospital were aware of the general rule. Testimony also showed that it is a duty of a nurse to report any critical condition to the doctor in charge, and if he or she does nothing, to then report the condition to his or her supervisor. Neither the nurses in the ICU nor the inhalation therapist told Dr. Weller that the tube was being left in longer than usual or reported Dr. Weller's treatment of Ms. Catron to their supervisors.

The court reviewed several cases where it was held that when a nurse or other hospital employee knows the doctor's orders are not in accordance with normal medical practice, it is the nurse's or other employee's duty to inform the attending physician. The trial court had said that a hospital is liable for negligent acts of its employees done within the scope of their employment. Therefore, a breach of employment duties under vicarious liability results in the liability of the hospital for negligent acts of its employee. The appellate court affirmed verdict of the trial court.

A nursing facility can be held liable under respondeat superior for nursing personnel failing to render proper care, treatment, or supervision of the residents and could have to pay damages for that negligence under vicarious liability. In *Doxey v. Riverside Guest Care Center*, 520 So 2d 1118, plaintiff Lessie Doxey, a resident at Riverside Guest Care Center, became acutely ill on December 25, 1983, from an ileus and urinary tract infection. This illness caused a condition where the plaintiff was unable to discharge waste from her body; her abdomen became distended and tender to the touch. When Mrs. Effie Froreich went to her sister's room, she observed that her sister was in severe distress, her abdomen being swollen, her face ashen, and an indwelling catheter not working. She became concerned and asked Nurse Breedlove several times for medical attention, to no avail. As the day progressed, Ms. Doxey's condition worsened, and her sister insisted that a doctor be called immediately. When the doctor did arrive the following evening, on December 26, upon examining the resident, he became angered that the nursing facility employees had allowed the resident's condition to deteriorate to such an extent before he was contacted. He admitted Ms. Doxey to a hospital that evening. She was later admitted to another nursing facility and has done quite well.

Mrs. Froreich, plaintiff's sister, filed suit on behalf of her sister against the Riverside Guest Care Center, saying that the nursing facility was negligent because its employees did not render proper care, treatment, or supervision. A nurse at the hospital testified that when Mrs. Doxey arrived, her abdomen was distended and she was very dirty. Her gown had been worn for several days and there was dried fecal material on her buttocks and a bad rash in her groin area; Mrs. Doxey had been wet and dirty for some time. The physician testified that if he had not intervened, the plaintiff would not have lived for more than 12–24 hours.

The appellate court said that it is the duty of a nursing facility to provide a reasonable standard of care, taking into account each resident's mental and physical condition. The court said that any human being having to endure this kind of neglect surely has undergone great mental and physical suffering. Fifty thousand dollars was awarded to the plaintiff.

A long-term care facility can be held liable if the acts of a physical therapist under its employ amount to negligence. In *Zucker v. Axelrod*, 527 NYS 2d 937, Judith Zucker, a licensed physical therapist employed by the nursing facility, refused to allow an 82-year-old resident to be excused for toileting prior to the treatment session. The physical therapist assumed that the resident was under a bowel and bladder training program and insisted that he stand at the parallel bars before he could be excused. The resident urinated while being assisted to stand at the bars. It was clear that the nursing facility had a policy of permitting residents to go to the bathroom whenever they expressed the need; other employees of the facility testified that they followed this policy.

The Supreme Court of New York State agreed with the findings of the administrative law judge that the physical therapist's refusal to excuse the resident in a timely fashion constituted resident neglect. The facility was held responsible for the negligent acts of the physical therapist.

The following cases point out the legal duty of a nursing facility to protect other residents from contagious diseases of fellow residents. In the nursing facility situation, most likely the resident does not have an infection when admitted to the facility, but in numerous instances, some of the residents contract an infection while in the facility. In these situations, the nurse and other personnel working with residents must use acceptable aseptic techniques.

In *Helman v. Sacred Heart Hospital*, 644 P 2d 605, Mr. Helman was injured in an automobile accident and suffered a crushed chest, dislocated hip, and multiple fractures. At the time of admission to the defendant hospital, he was placed in a semiprivate room. The other patient in the room suffered from a fractured back and was paralyzed from the waist down. The plaintiff was subjected to extensive surgery on his hip while in the hospital. About eight days later, his roommate complained of a boil under his arm. The boil drained after applications of hot compresses; a culture was taken, submitted to the lab for analysis, and determined to be staph infection. On the first day following surgery, Mr. Helman developed a fever. Between the time that the other patient suffered from the boil and the time he was removed to the isolation room, the nurses and hospital attendants treated both patients on a regular basis—changing the sheets and dressings, giving back rubs, etc. The personnel attending both patients did not use proper sterile techniques, failing to wash their hands or to leave the room between treatments. It was determined by a culture that the plaintiff was now also suffering from staph infection that had penetrated into his hip socket and destroyed bone and tissue, requiring another operative procedure. Mr. Helman sued the hospital for injuries resulting from a staphylococcus infection acquired in the hospital through cross-infection from another patient.

The court discussed the duty of a well-run health care facility regarding infections and indicated that all facilities should be alert to the danger of cross-infection by staph coagulase positive infections among their patients and residents and of the serious consequences caused. Infection control committees are maintained to trace and isolate infections and personnel are trained in sterile techniques. The court indicated that, if a person placed his or her hands in an area near an open wound containing staph and then later placed his or her hands on another patient, this patient would likely be exposed to massive transfer of bacteria. Sacred Heart Hospital had techniques and rules requiring all medical personnel to report open wounds among patients and hospital personnel. Expert witnesses indicated the staphylococcus infections differed. Although, on cross-examination, their statements were inconsistent, the court felt there was sufficient evidence to prove the necessary causal relationship to have caused the injuries. Judgment was rendered for the plaintiff in the amount of $67,839.97.

In *Kalmus v. Cedars of Lebanon Hospital*, 281 P 2d 872, a patient was given an injection to relax her nerves with an unsterile needle, causing a staphylococcus aureus hemolytic infection. The court held that the personnel violated the standard operating procedure; therefore, the hospital was negligent.

In *Woodlawn Infirmary v. Byers*, 112 So 831, an action was brought to recover for the death of plaintiff's daughter from lockjaw, allegedly acquired after an appendicitis operation. The plaintiff said the infirmary had used unsterile instruments in the surgery and brooms instead of mops to sweep floors, causing great amounts of dust. Evidence showed that another patient in the hospital had died of tetanus just a few days before. Because of technicalities concerning the admission of other necessary evidence, the court ruled in favor of the defendant.

Staphylococcus infections in hospitals and nursing facilities are quite common. However, recovery against health care facilities is difficult in infection cases. It is hard to prove the direct cause of the injury under the ordinary rules of negligence; it is difficult to obtain the evidence to prove the causal relationship. To overcome these difficulties, plaintiffs' attorneys are attempting to recover under the theory of res ipsa loquitur. If this rule is allowed to prevail in infection cases, evidence of negligence may be established without proof of the negligence by expert witnesses. Three conditions must be met to apply the doctrine of res ipsa loquitur.

1. The act allegedly causing the injury must be in control of the nursing facility or subject to its use and inspection.
2. The injury could not have happened except through the negligence of the nursing facility.
3. The resident did not contribute in any way to the cause of the resulting injury.

Guidelines for Policies Concerning Infections

A nursing facility may protect its legal interests and its residents from the injury or harm caused by infections by the following means:

- Have written infection control policies in effect in the nursing facility.
- Adhere strictly to the policies placed in effect.
- Use internal inservice orientation and training programs highlighting education of all personnel.
- Emphasize the necessity to all personnel of observing clinical changes in residents and reporting them to qualified professionals.
- Establish a program whereby any breach of the infection control policy is reported to the administration.

CHAPTER 5

Corporate Negligence

The term *corporate liability* is somewhat misleading as it applies to health care facilities. Corporate liability is based on the theory that the facility itself owes legal duties to those coming into contact with it. Such liability occurs when a facility breaches or violates one or more of these duties and is determined negligent.

The doctrine of corporate negligence imposes a direct responsibility on the long-term care facility to act in a nonnegligent manner. Under this doctrine, liability may be imposed upon individuals who are not employees of the facility, such as those serving on governing bodies of a sole proprietorship, partnership, or corporation. In the law relating to corporate duties, the same principles apply to long-term care facilities and hospitals.

The term *governing body* applies, in the legal sense, to different types of business entities. In all business entities, the individual(s) composing the governing body may be held liable for duties violated. In the health care industry, facilities are sole proprietorships, partnerships, or corporations. The governing body of a sole proprietorship is the individual owner; of a partnership, its general partners; and of a corporation, the individual members of its board of directors.

For the purpose of establishing corporate negligence, the courts have discussed the general duties of ownership owed to persons coming into contact with the business entity. The law categorizes these persons as business invitees, licensees, and trespassers.

- A *business invitee* is one who comes to the facility to conduct business on the premises primarily for the benefit of the owner. The duty owed by the facility to a business invitee is to exercise reasonable care and to warn the invitee of any dangerous conditions on the premises. Residents, employees, and the general public are considered business invitees.

- A *licensee* is one who has express or implied consent of the owner to enter the property but whose presence does not benefit the owner. The duty owed by the facility to a licensee is to warn of any existing or potentially dangerous conditions on the premises. A group of persons allowed on the premises to solicit funds for its own benefit is considered a licensee.

- A *trespasser* is one who comes on the premises without the express or implied consent of the owner. The duty owed by the facility to a trespasser is only to give warning of highly dangerous conditions and to refrain from wanton and willful conduct that will cause injury to the trespasser.

The basic functions of the governing body include:

- selection and appointment of its corporate officers and agents
- general control of the compensation of such agents
- establishment of policies and procedures in the facility
- supervision and protection of the assets of the business
- delegation of authority to the CEO/administrator of the facility

In addition, the governing body of all facilities owes the following specific duties to those coming into contact with it:

- Provide adequate facilities and equipment.
- Maintain buildings and grounds in proper conditions.
- Select, retain, and supervise employees.
- Provide satisfactory resident care.
- Provide adequate staff.
- Protect against falls.
- Comply with statutory rules and regulations of regulatory agencies.
- Provide a safe environment for residents and employees.

DUTY TO PROVIDE ADEQUATE FACILITIES AND EQUIPMENT

The Code of Federal Regulations (42 CFR, Part 483.70, 10/1/98) states that health care facilities must be designed, constructed, equipped, and maintained to protect the health and safety of their residents and personnel and the public. Areas of importance include compliance with the Life Safety Code, an emergency power system, and adequate space and equipment in dining, health services, recreation, and resident rooms.

Within the duty to provide adequate facilities and equipment, the governing body must exercise reasonable care and skill in supervising and managing the facility property and make certain that the equipment needed to treat residents is available and in good working order.

In the case of *Williams v. Orange Memorial Hospital*, 202 S 2d 859, the plaintiff was admitted to the hospital for treatment of severe headaches. While in the hospital, she requested that the nurse give her something for constipation. She was given a suppository but stated that she was unable to have a bowel movement on the bedpan while the pan was on the bed. The nurse brought a straight-backed chair and placed the bedpan on it. When the patient lowered herself onto the pan, the chair broke and she fell to the floor, injuring her side and back. The patient sued the hospital for personal injuries as a result of the incident, maintaining that she was a patient in the hospital and entitled to receive proper care and provision of safe equipment. Because of her unusual condition at the time, she could not check the condition of the chair before she sat on the bedpan.

The court agreed, saying that when a patient enters a hospital, there is at least an implied agreement to provide proper care. The chair in question was under the exclusive control of the hospital; the plaintiff was sick, constipated, and in no condition to inspect the chair before sitting on it. The court concluded that this was sufficient evidence to warrant liability of the hospital for corporate negligence in furnishing to the patient defective equipment for her care and allowed the case to go to the jury.

In *Holtforth v. Rochester General Hospital*, 105 NE 2d 610, a patient was injured because of a defective locking device on a wheelchair that caused the chair to tip over. The court, in determining that the facility was liable for corporate negligence, said that the patient could expect the hospital to use reasonable care in the selection and maintenance of wheelchairs being used in the facility.

These cases point out that facilities have a corporate duty to see that all equipment used in conjunction with their services is in proper working condition and is not overtly defective. One way a nursing facility can ensure that its equipment is in proper condition is to implement a preventive maintenance program. Under such a program, all equipment is routinely checked for defects to make sure it is in proper working condition. The person checking the equipment keeps a preventive maintenance record listing: each item checked, the time, the date, and the name of the person checking the equipment.

The cases also indicate that even if a piece of equipment is not overtly defective, corporate negligence may occur when personnel are not adequately trained in the use of the equipment and to know when it is not working properly. Therefore, it is important that a nursing facility have an ongoing inservice training program for personnel on the use and working condition of any equipment the center has in operation.

DUTY TO MAINTAIN BUILDINGS AND GROUNDS IN PROPER CONDITION

These cases point out the duty of a health care facility is to warn all who come in contact with it of any dangerous or potentially dangerous conditions whereby a resident or visitor could foreseeably be injured. It is also necessary that personnel be trained in safe grounds- and housekeeping techniques—for example, posting warning signs, blocking off areas that are being wet-mopped, etc.

In *Penland v. Brentwood Rehabilitation Center*, 260 SE 2d 678, boxes stored in the east wing hallway of the nursing facility created an obstruction. A nurse employed by the facility had said that these boxes were dangerous to persons walking in the hallway area. Subsequently, the nurse tripped on the boxes and was injured.

The court said that it is the duty of the facility to keep the premises in a reasonably safe condition so as to not unnecessarily expose those in the area to danger. The court concluded, "In this case, there is substantial evidence from which a jury could find that the hallway in the east wing had an obstruction in which it was dangerous to persons walking in the hallway."

In *St. Vincent's Hospital v. Crouch*, 292 S 2d 405, Hetty Crouch, the wife of a patient in the hospital, was 68 years old and in good health. While visiting her husband earlier on the day of her accident, she observed workmen removing a sawhorse barricade from the hospital main parking lot. She returned to the hospital about 6:00 that evening. After parking, she got out of her automobile and had to sidle forward due to the narrow space between her car and the car to her left. As she approached the front of her car, her foot hit a small raised pile of concrete building material, causing her to fall between the two cars. She sustained a fractured hip, resulting in septic neurosis of the hip and ambulation only with the use of a walker or wheelchair. Mrs. Crouch brought action against the hospital and contractor for maintaining a parking lot in a negligent manner.

The court, in considering the case, stated that the plaintiff occupied the status of a business invitee at the time of the accident. Mrs. Crouch testified that she was looking ahead as she sidled between the cars; the court said that under these circumstances, she did not have a duty to keep her eyes on the ground and, therefore, was not contributorily negligent to her injury. Mrs. Crouch assumed that there was no dangerous condition in the parking lot, as she had observed the sawhorse barricade being removed. The court felt that even though this barricade had been removed earlier in the day, the parking lot was still in a hazardous condition. The court indicated that the hospital had a duty to continue to warn any business invitees coming onto its property of conditions that are dangerous or potentially hazardous. Mrs. Crouch was awarded $250,000 in damages.

DUTY TO SELECT, RETAIN, AND SUPERVISE EMPLOYEES

The duty to properly select the employees who are to be hired to work in a long-term care facility is very important. Some of the facility's responsibilities in this area are to check references of new applicants being considered for employment, to appropriately assign employees according to their background and experience, and to supervise the employees once they are hired.

The case of *Deerings West Nursing Center v. Velma Pander Scott*, 787 SW 2d 494, discussed the issue of negligent hiring. Immediately prior to working as a nurse employee at the nursing facility, Ken Hopper, a 36-year-old 6'4" male, was a bartender at the Queen of Hearts bar. In his application for employment, he falsely stated that he had a Texas LVN (licensed vocational nurse) license and that he had not been convicted of a crime. In fact, he was not licensed and had committed over 56 offenses of theft. He was on probation at the time of his hiring.

Velma Pander Scott, an 80-year-old woman, made it a habit to come to the facility at all hours to visit her infirm older brother. One morning,

Ken Hopper attempted to prevent her from visiting. Scott threw up her hands in defense upon his approach, but she was hit on the chin. Hopper slapped her down, followed her to the floor, and pinned her there with his knees upon her chest. She brought an action against the facility for the resulting injuries sustained.

Hopper testified that he was hired for the supervisory nursing position sight unseen over the phone by the director of nursing. A witness, who worked as a nurse aide for the facility, felt that the facility had an obligation to check and verify the existence of an LVN license.

In its opinion, the court enunciated the facility's duty to the public. The law, under the doctrine of negligent hiring, is that the employer is responsible for his or her own negligence in hiring or retaining an employee whom the employer should have known to be incompetent by exercising judgment. Considering the nature of its business, the nursing facility owes a high degree of care to select competent employees and to refrain from hiring those who are unfit. This employer was liable even though the injury was brought about by the employee's willful act, which was beyond the scope of his employment.

The court then discussed an additional breach by the nursing facility of the statutes of the State of Texas. The court cited the Nursing Home Administration Licensure Act, which states that the facility must oversee the examination and education of both LVNs and administrators. The Texas statute emphasizes that applicants must be of good moral character. The facility had violated the purpose of the licensing statute by hiring an unfit, incompetent person who was certainly without "good moral character." In addition, the facility had placed him in a position of authority as a supervisor, which allowed him to dispense drugs.

The appellate court of Texas upheld the jury finding against the facility of $35,000 in actual damages and $200,000 in punitive damages for gross negligence in hiring an unlicensed nurse employee, who assaulted an 80-year-old visitor to the facility.

The case of *William N. Jones Memorial Hospital v. David*, 553 SW 2d 180, concerns an action brought against the hospital for injuries sustained due to an orderly's negligent attempt to remove a catheter from the plaintiff. Leslie C. Looman sought employment as an orderly with the hospital. He completed the employment application; his list of references included Johnson & Johnson, where he had been employed as a forklift operator, and the U.S. Navy, where he said he served as a medical corpsman for eight months. Looman was interviewed by the associate director of nursing. He was hired at the completion of the interview and told to report for work prior to any reference check because of a critical need for orderlies. The hiring policy of the hospital called for obtaining at least one employment and one personal reference before hiring an applicant. Inquiry was later made to Johnson & Johnson, who verified that Looman had worked there but did not answer questions about why Looman left his job, his dependability, his attitude, his job knowledge, and whether or not they would reemploy him. The hospital did not check the U.S. Navy reference because it claimed it had not received any cooperation from the armed services in the past.

David entered the hospital for a transurethral resection of his prostate. The surgical procedure was performed shortly after his admission. A few days after the operation, orderly Looman attempted to remove a Foley catheter from the plaintiff's bladder without first deflating the ball that held it in place. The patient stopped the orderly and instructed him to call a nurse to properly remove the catheter. David sustained serious personal damage to his sphincter muscle as a result of the orderly's attempt to remove the catheter. He sued the hospital and the orderly, alleging that the orderly had failed to use ordinary care in his attempt to remove the catheter and was unfit to perform the duties of an orderly in this area and that the hospital was reckless in the employment and selection of the orderly.

The court stated that hiring policies enable the hospital to evaluate an applicant's experience, qualifications, and character independently of the applicant's representations in order to prevent incompetent and unfit employees from injuring patients. The court's opinion pointed out that the fact that Johnson & Johnson had failed to answer critical questions on the reference form was sufficient to put the hospital on notice that a follow-up was necessary. The plaintiff secured Looman's naval records within 10 days of request and found that he had been expelled from the Navy after one month's training and had a serious drug problem and criminal record. The court said, "Here we have, for all practical purposes, a complete disregard and a complete violation of the stated hiring policies of the hospital. . . . The hospital demonstrated an entire want of care as to indicate that the hiring of Looman was the result of conscious indifference to the rights, welfare, and safety of the patients." Had the hospital checked Looman's reference, as dictated by policy, it would have found him unfit to work at the hospital. The plaintiff was awarded $17,000 in actual damages and $18,000 in punitive damages.

Good administration demands that a conscientious effort be made to check all references before an applicant is hired. The employees in the above mentioned cases were negligent and the facilities were held liable under vicarious liability. In addition, corporate liability was imposed upon the facilities, as they had breached the corporate duty relative to the hiring of competent personnel to treat and serve residents and patients. All health care facilities should have written policies regarding reference checks and see to it that these policies are strictly adhered to in order to avoid such financial and legal liabilities as were imposed in these cases.

In the case of *Eugene Merriman v. New York State Department of Mental Health*, 282 NYS 2d 167, the petitioner, Merriman, had been found guilty of four out of five charges of physical abuse of incompetent residents of the Rome State School; the hearing officer recommended that he be suspended without pay for two months. However, Dr. Bucholtz, the acting director of the school, terminated Merriman's employment immediately, finding that his behavior was motivated by pure malice. Merriman appealed the hearing officer's decision to the New York State Supreme Court.

At the Supreme Court hearing, Robert Cook, a trooper with the New York State Police, was the sole witness presented in support of the specifications as outlined by the Rome State School. He testified that he worked as an undercover agent at the school for three months, during which he was introduced to Merriman and observed his behavior toward the following patients in Ward 184:

- *February 2nd*—Mr. Caldwell was sitting on the floor of the day room screaming with a very hoarse voice. Merriman, the petitioner, walked over and struck him with his fist in the forehead with sufficient force to snap his head back.
- *February 11th*—Mr. Palamaro was sitting in a rocking chair in the day room. The petitioner walked up to Palamaro, wiped his shoes on his trousers, and struck him in the face and back several times with his fists.
- *February 14th*—Palamaro was again sitting in the rocking chair in the day room with his feet clad in slippers. The petitioner stepped on Palamaro's feet, grinding the toes of his shoes into the tops of his feet. He then used his heel in a like manner. Palamaro jumped out of his chair yelling obscenities.
- *February 14th*—The petitioner and Trooper Cook were sitting in the clothes room when Mr. Buchanan walked in. The petitioner yelled to Buchanan to get out of the clothes room, got out of his chair, and struck Buchanan in the stomach.

Charlotte Coleman, a registered nurse at the school, testified that she knew Merriman before being transferred to another department. She stated that Merriman was helpful, kind, and interested in the patients and that she had never seen him strike Caldwell, Palamaro, or Buchanan.

Merriman, the petitioner, testified in his own behalf. He stated that he had worked for the school for approximately eight years, that he had a wife and five children, and that he did not strike any of the patients listed in the specification.

The court indicated that the primary issue was the appropriateness of the penalty imposed by the acting director. It concluded that, after considering all the testimony, the penalty of dismissal is not disproportionate to the effects, does not shock one's sense of fairness, and comes well within the discretionary authority of the acting director to protect the patients within his charge from physical and mental abuse. The New York State Supreme Court then affirmed the decision of the hearing officer.

This case points out that while a health care facility is not the ensurer of the safety of its residents, it does have a duty to provide a reasonable standard of care and must supervise employees to ensure that residents are not harmed or abused.

DUTY TO PROVIDE SATISFACTORY RESIDENT CARE

In the average long-term care facility, residents may suffer from lapse of memory or senility. The intensity of these emotional disturbances may range from maladjustment to psychosis. If the resident is not a threat to him- herself or a danger to other residents, there is very little probability of liability to the facility. Conversely, the potential liability to the facility increases in direct proportion to the erratic behavior of residents affecting other residents.

The duty owed to a resident has been interpreted to mean that long-term health care facilities must render reasonable care and attention, taking into consideration the mental and physical condition of the residents, to protect the safety of both residents and others in the facility. There is an implied responsibility to maintain sufficient staffing and equipment to supervise and protect residents from potential hazards. Several areas covered under the duty to comply with acceptable standards of care owed to residents are protecting the resident from acquiring or aggravating bedsores, the use of bedrails, and protection of residents from harming self and others. The following cases indicate some factors the courts consider in determining possible negligence on the part of the health care facility.

Duty To Provide Adequate Staff

To carry out its purpose, a nursing facility must hire full-time, part-time, and consulting staff who are trained and licensed, certified, or registered according to profession and state law. It is imperative that orientation, ongoing inservices training, review, and supervision are provided to ensure the adherence to related policies and the quality of the environment and services.

The petitioner in *Czubinsky v. Doctors Hospital*, 1988 California Reporter 685, while recovering from anesthesia, went into cardiac arrest, which resulted in permanent injuries. The court of appeals found that the injuries sustained by Ms. Czubinsky were the direct result of the hospital personnel's failure to properly monitor and render the aid needed in the immediate postoperative period. The RN assigned to Czubinsky had a duty to remain with her until she was transferred to the recovery room. The nurse's absence at this time was the approximate cause of the petitioner's injuries. The failure of the hospital to provide adequate staff when needed was ruled dereliction of duty.

Montgomery Health Care Facility v. Ella Ballard, 565 So 2d 221, involved a lawsuit brought on behalf of the plaintiff against the Montgomery Health Care Facility and its parent company, First American Health Care, Inc.

Mrs. Stoval was admitted to the nursing facility on February 8, 1985, suffering from several chronic diseases; no bedsores were noted on her admitting physical examination. The first record of a bedsore was on February 14, 1985. On two occasions after her admission, she was sent to the hospital for surgical removal of decubitus ulcers on her hip, upper left thigh, and left heel. Stoval died in the hospital on March 4, 1986. The resulting lawsuit claimed that Stoval died as a result of the defendant facility's negligence whereby she suffered multiple infected bedsores.

Evidence was presented of at least 17 deficiencies ranging from lack of ongoing treatment of the resident for bedsores to improper handling of linen. Additionally, there was evidence of inadequate staffing where the director of nurses was not responsible for standards of nursing practice and charge nurses were not responsible for supervision of nursing activities. The governing body management, through the administrator, had not enforced rules and regulations concerning the resident's health and safety, resident care policies, and infection control. The jury concluded that the evidence admitted was directly related to the development of the pressure sores from which Stoval died.

The jury assessed the facility punitive damages in the amount of two million dollars which the defendants argued was greater than necessary to punish them. The court responded, "Because of the large number of nursing home residents vulnerable to the type of neglect found in this case, the verdict would further the goal of discouraging others from similar conduct in the future."

Duty To Protect Against Falls

Falls by residents may occur by a failure to restrain, supervise, or attend the resident.

In *Knutson v. Life Care Communities, Inc.*, 493 So 2d 1133, a nursing facility resident sued the facility for damages to her hip as a result of a fall out of bed. She recovered because of the facility's negligence to properly attend to her needs during convalescence.

In the case of *Crawford v. Long Memorial Hospital*, 66 SE 2d 63, an action was brought against the facility for damages resulting from injuries sustained when the plaintiff, a patient, fell on a slippery floor. The patient was admitted to the hospital for anemia and general weakness requiring blood transfusions. The day before the accident, the floors of the patient's room and bathroom were mopped by one of the maintenance employees. An excessive amount of soap and cleaning compound was used and not completely removed from the floors at the finish of the job. The next morning, on the day of the accident, an orderly went into the patient's bathroom to get water to fill water pitchers for other patients. While doing so, he spilled water on the bathroom floor, which became slippery because of the compound left on the day before. Later that day the patient was given an enema and was compelled to relieve herself. She walked into the bathroom, slipped on the floor, and hit against the bathtub, injuring herself.

The court held that the facility had a duty to maintain the floors in patient areas in a condition that would not endanger those using the facility. The maintenance personnel's use of excessive cleaning compound and the orderly's spilling of water, which rendered the floor slippery, amounted to corporate negligence on the part of the facility. The court found that the center must compensate the patient in damages for her injury.

Use of Restraints

The practice of using restraints on elderly residents in nursing facilities has been widespread for the past 100 years. Today, approximately 41 percent of residents are subject to physical restraints; 93 percent of those who are placed into restraints remain in them for the duration of their nursing facility stay.

There is a growing professional and public perception that the use of physical restraints in nursing facilities is unnecessary in many instances. In response, the Omnibus Budget Reconciliation Act (OBRA) 1987 regulations and recent Health Care Financing Administration (HCFA) initiatives are working to bring about a greatly reduced reliance on the use of physical restraints in nursing facilities.

In response to the fear of liability resulting from reduced use of restraints, Professor Johnson studied a variety of nursing facility cases, of which four involved residents who wandered and 60 involved residents who were injured by falls. Most of these cases resulted in judgment for the nursing facility. Generally, the courts are holding that where resident injury takes place in spite of facility compliance with applicable federal and state regulations regarding the safeguarding of residents, the legal standard of care has been satisfied.

> In *Kildren v. Shady Oaks Nursing Home*, 549 So 2d 395, Mr. Kildren, a facility resident, fell and fractured his hip while unrestrained and unattended. Professional judgment had been made to use restraints as sparingly as possible because they made the resident hostile. His medical record reflected two previous falls, neither of which had resulted in serious injury. The family brought a lawsuit against the facility based on negligence.
> While the trial court found for the family, the appeals court reversed the decision and said, "The nursing facility is not the insurer of the safety of its residents. The standard of care imposed upon a nursing facility is that of reasonable care, considering the resident's known mental and physical condition."

A good number of cases regarding unrestrained residents have followed the same legal principle—that nursing facilities do not have the duty to restrain residents. Where liability has been found for injuries resulting from the absence of restraints, courts are encouraging the use of less restrictive alternatives rather than mandating the use of restraints.

DUTY TO COMPLY WITH STATUTORY RULES AND REGULATIONS OF REGULATORY AGENCIES

The governing body and its authorized agents are responsible for compliance with federal, state, and local rules and regulations regarding the operation of a nursing facility. The following cases point out the importance of using the required alarm systems and of supervising residents whose tendency to wander is known to the staff.

> The event precipitating in *Helen H. Fields v. Senior Citizens Center, Inc.*, 528 So 2d 573, occurred when a 68-year-old resident of the center, William Fields, left the premises of the facility unattended. When crossing a street, he was struck and killed by a van driven by his daughter. Helen Fields, the victim's widow, sued the nursing facility for the death of

her husband based on its failure to properly supervise him, knowing that he was a wandering resident.

Several witnesses testified at the trial that:

- Mr. Fields got lost often in the facility.
- On admission to the facility, Mr. Fields' mental state was one of confusion and disorientation.
- Although there was a security system, it was not turned on at the time of the incident.
- The nurses had been told to watch Mr. Fields closely.

The jury found the nursing facility to be negligent and awarded $200,000 in damages to the widow. The appellate court upheld the lower court, finding that:

- The standard of care imposed upon a facility is that of reasonable care considering the resident's mental and physical condition.
- A nursing facility's duty to its residents generally does not include having an attendant follow an ambulatory resident at all times. However, a facility is required to take reasonable steps to prevent injury to ambulatory and mentally confused residents.
- In this case, the facility had an alarm system that it failed to use properly; the system had not been activated as required.
- The physical layout of the building prevented observation of the front door by staff members at the nurses' station, thereby allowing residents to leave without proper supervision.
- The award of $200,000 to the surviving spouse was reasonable for loss of love, affection, and income.

In *Nolan V. Booty et al. v. Kentwood Manor Nursing Home, Inc.*, 483 So 2d 634, a similar incident occurred. At the time of admission, Mr. Booty was 90 years old, ambulatory, mentally confused, and unable to properly care for himself. Often, Booty would leave, or attempt to leave, the facility and wander about outside. His confused mental state and habit of wandering was well known to the entire nursing staff. The facility had a buzzer alarm system that went off if a resident left the facility. During the day and throughout the evening, the doors to the facility remained propped open for the convenience of the staff; the alarm system was not activated until 11:00 P.M. At 10:15 P.M., on the day that Booty left the facility and fell down an embankment, fractured his hip, and subsequently died, the alarm system was not activated. The plaintiff alleged that the nursing facility failed to adequately supervise and provide for the safety of Booty.

The court held that the duty of care owed by a facility to its residents is to provide a reasonable standard of care, taking into consideration each resident's known mental and physical condition. Facilities are to take reasonable steps to prevent injury to ambulatory residents who are mentally confused and physically fragile. In this case, Booty's confused mental state and habit of wandering were well known to the entire staff. While the facility had an alarm system to safeguard its wandering residents, the system was not activated solely for the convenience of the facility staff and thereby rendered useless. The court awarded damages to the plaintiff's widow and daughter in the amount of $38,901.29 each.

DUTY TO PROVIDE A SAFE ENVIRONMENT FOR RESIDENTS AND EMPLOYEES

Today, a nursing facility may be held liable for injuries both to employees who work in the facility and to residents of the facility. A facility whose building is of unsafe construction or in disrepair or that has inadequate staff could have its license to operate revoked.

In *Erie Care Center v. Ackerman*, 449 NE 2d 486, a hearing officer was appointed by the Department of Health to conduct a nursing facility licensure revocation because of numerous violations. The violations included disrepair of the building, inadequate medical records, nursing staff shortage, and uncleanliness of the facility. The hearing officer recommended that the operator's license be revoked. The case was then appealed to the Court of Appeals of Ohio, which held that there was substantial evidence of the multiple violations to justify revocation of the operator's license.

In *Slocum v. Berman*, 439 NYS 2d 967, Eleanor Slocum, the operator of Maple Lawn Nursing Home, owned a two-story woodframe nursing facility that has been operating since 1958. A hearing officer found that the structure was not fire protected or fire resistant and that these violations adversely affected the safety and welfare of the occupants. After appeal, the state supreme court said there was substantial evidence of the violations to support revocation of the facility's operating license.

CHAPTER 6

The Governing Body

Nursing facilities in the United States are regulated by both federal and state laws. Long-term care facilities may operate as a sole proprietorship, a partnership, or a corporation; most of them today are incorporate. The typical facility is incorporated by state law as a for-profit or nonprofit corporation. This means that the facility must comply with all rules and regulations relating to the business, including the important duty to appoint a qualified administrator.

The Code of Federal Regulations, 42 CFR, Chap IV, Part 430 to end, 10-1-98, states that the facility must have a governing body that is legally responsible for establishing and implementing policies regarding the management and operation of the facility. The governing body of a proprietorship is the proprietor; of a partnership, all the partners; and of a for-profit or nonprofit corporation, the board of directors. The governing body has ultimate responsibility and authority for the operation of the facility.

Following is a discussion of the organization, duties, and responsibilities of the corporate governing body or board of directors.

ORGANIZATION OF THE BOARD OF DIRECTORS

Size

Generally speaking, the size of the governing board should be adequate to meet the needs of a community. The size differs depending upon the type of institution—whether it is a hospital or nursing facility , or a proprietary

71

or nonprofit corporation. Some skilled nursing facilities have large boards in order to obtain a broad contact with the community. However, with a large board, it may be difficult to reach decisions and to find qualified individuals to serve on the board. The number on governing boards varies from 3 to 30 persons, with the average numbering about 15. It has been determined that this number is a manageable size. Some organizations add advisory boards for community reaction, but this could prove dangerous and promote duplication unless the role and the functions of the advisory board are clearly and concisely defined.

Qualifications

If possible, a broad representation of disciplines should be on the board of directors. Lawyers, physicians, educators, laborers, businesspersons, and consumers are the types of community leaders desired. At one time, it was almost heresy to allow a physician on a board, but today it is becoming a customary practice. It is also customary to involve consumers of health care on the board of directors.

Members, whether professional, business, or labor representatives, should be chosen on the basis of proven leadership qualities in the community, not as patronage for a favor done for the nursing facility. A business owner who is a leader in the community might have certain organizational abilities. A lawyer may or may not be the attorney for the health care facility. If retained by the health care facility, he or she should not be asked to give formal legal opinions at board meetings but can be used as a guide regarding legal implications involved in setting policy in the health care facility. A physician on the board should represent the feelings of the physicians in the community, not those of colleagues with an axe to grind with administration or with other colleagues. This selection should be based on individual qualities, not merely because the person is a doctor. The labor leader can be of valuable assistance in determining policy regarding the benefits the health care facility wishes to offer its employees. Some boards appoint a certified public accountant or a financial analyst to assist in general financial issues.

Board members should be successful in their respective fields. If a person is a failure in his or her own profession or business, the chances are he or she will not be of much assistance on the board of directors. Members of the board must be honest and above reproach and free from political influence. Avoid selecting controversial politicians in the community; decisions on policy matters might be based on political expedience instead of on what will benefit the health care facility. Finally, board members should not be so aggressive that they will not allow the chief executive officer to manage the facility. On the other hand, they should not be rubber stamps or avoid participation in the activities of the health care facility.

Methods

The boards of directors are elected by the shareholders of proprietary for-profit corporations; they are appointed by the ownership of nonprofit corporations. The nonprofit health care facility should select an independent board of interested citizens, appointed for a specific term of years. Many organizations appoint one-third of the members for three years, one-third for two years, and one-third for one year; continuity of function is maintained as all terms are not completed at the same time. Another method is one-year appointments, subject to annual reappointment. This method leaves the possibility of breaking continuity if few reappointments are made.

COMMITTEES OF THE BOARD OF DIRECTORS

Board committees assist the governing body in specific areas with varying degrees of management and advisory functions; most effective functions include the development of strategy and policy. Generally, an ideal committee size is five members with adequate skills and knowledge to deal with the committee subject matter. This number seems to give balance between too many interested persons and not enough persons to represent all facets. It is important that the committee be workable, promoting deliberation and ability to reach group decisions by an integration of ideas without weak compromise or power politics. Committee members need to know the scope of the subjects to be considered and if they are responsible for reaching decisions, making recommendations, or deliberating for insight into a problem. The chairperson ensures that the committee acts effectively.

Committees of the board may fall into two broad categories: standing and ad hoc. *Standing committees* are of a permanent nature and are designed to carry out, in a general way, the statutory responsibilities of the board of directors. *Ad hoc committees* are established to carry out a specific purpose; they cease to exist when that purpose is complete. Ad hoc committees include nominating committees, special fund-raising committees, and survey and study committees.

Standing Committees

The **executive committee** usually consists of the officers of the corporation and several directors at large. Some organizations include the immediate past president as a member of this committee. When the board of directors is large, this committee may serve as the authority to whom the administration must report. On decisions of a major nature, such as the dissolution of the corporation, major building programs, and capital financing efforts, this committee's actions should be ratified and approved by the full board. When the board meets quarterly or less often, it becomes important that the executive committee meet monthly to carry out the activities of the health care facility. If the board is a small group and if it meets monthly, the functions of the executive committee then become less vital inasmuch as members should then deliberate on matters of an emergency nature.

The **finance committee** should be composed of three to five members who, ideally, have a background in business, law, or accounting. One of the major functions of this committee is to review the annual budget, which is prepared and submitted to the board of directors by the administrator, and to submit a recommendation concerning the budget to the full board. Also, this committee may review with the administrator the salary and wage program being conducted in the facility and take necessary steps if the health facility is planning to borrow money for expansion of its services.

The **public relations committee** should consist of three to five members who, ideally, have a background in journalism, psychology, or basic knowledge of human relations. This committee is important in the small health care facility because nursing facilities do not generally retain a full-time public relations director. The public image of the health care facility is vital. For too many years, nursing facilities have had a poor public image because the community receives insufficient information regarding their activities. One person on the committee should regularly prepare news releases and human interest stories for the news media. Any innovation or interesting procedure as well as any new equipment used in the facility should be explained to the community. Millions of dollars are expended by private corporations to improve their image and yet, in the health care field, we generally do not have a systematic approach to this important function.

The **building committee** should be composed of two to three members and should assist the administration when building plans are being projected or remodeling or renovation is anticipated. Individuals active in building and real estate in the community might serve as members of this committee.

The **fund-raising committee** might assist in any continuing fund-raising projects as well as special projects undertaken by the health care facility.

The **joint conference committee** is important in hospitals and skilled nursing facilities. Its members should include several officers of the board of directors, the administrator of the facility, and several officers of the organized medical staff. It serves as an excellent method of communication to the board of directors regarding activities of a medico-administrative nature. This committee is required by the Joint Commission on Accreditation of Healthcare Organizations, the Public Health Service, and other regulatory agencies.

Ad Hoc Committees

The **nominating committee** is usually appointed by the president of the corporation and is concerned with the nomination of new officers as well as the board members of a health care facility. After a slate of officers is presented to the board, this committee is normally dissolved.

The **survey and study committee** undertakes special studies or projects that the health facility might desire to have completed. Community image studies might be a function of this committee.

MEETINGS OF THE BOARD OF DIRECTORS

Meetings of the board of directors may be categorized into the following types: regular meetings, special meetings, and annual meetings. The board of directors, ideally, meets monthly to carry on the management of the health facility. These meetings are general in nature and may be set up in the following manner:

1. Call to order
2. Reading of minutes of previous meeting
3. Old business
4. Communications
5. New business
6. Reports of officers and committees
7. Adjournment

Special meetings may be called by the officers or by a designated member of the board as provided for in the articles of incorporation and bylaws of the health care facility. For example, some bylaws provide that the president may call a special meeting if adequate notice is given. The time considered adequate may be anywhere from 3 days to 30 days. Usually, the bylaws provide that the reason for the special meeting be indicated in the notice sent to the board of directors, and there is generally a provision stating that only the business of the special meeting should be heard.

The annual meeting is called to elect new officers and to receive reports from the administrator regarding the operation of the facility. The annual report should outline, by department, the activities in the health care facility during the past year. This fiscal report is also discussed and the financial operation of the health care facility is then reviewed. The annual budget, including salary budget, supplies and expense budget, and equipment budget, may be discussed at this meeting.

DUTIES AND RESPONSIBILITIES OF THE BOARD OF DIRECTORS

General Duties

Directors of a corporation must act in good faith and for the best interests of the corporation or health care facility. They must use due and reasonable care, exercise diligence, and act within the scope of authority conferred upon them. Directors are expected to keep themselves informed as to the general type of business in which the corporation is engaged and to be knowledgeable about the corporation's business activities. It is the duty of the directors to ensure that their health facility obeys the law and maintains its activities within the corporate powers.

Directors are treated as **fiduciaries** with respect to the corporation. Their relationship to the health care facility involves responsibility and accountability. It is their duty to administer the corporate affairs for the common benefit of all the stockholders and exercise their best care, skill, and judgment in the management of the corporation.

Three general duties are defined by cases handed down by the courts.

1. A duty of **obedience**, meaning that the directors are supposed to perform their activities within the powers conferred upon the corporation by its bylaws and articles of incorporation. The courts have pointed out that the willful violation of this duty may make the director liable to the corporation.
2. A duty of **diligence**, meaning that directors should exercise that degree of care that the reasonably prudent person would exercise under the same or similar circumstances as to the general management of the corporation.
3. A duty of **loyalty**, meaning that directors must refrain from engaging in their personal activities in such a manner as to injure or take advantage of the health facility. That is, the directors of a corporation may not make secret or private profits out of their official positions and must give the corporation the benefit of any advantages they may gain due to their relationship of trust with the corporation.

Specific Duties

The board of directors must:

- Establish the overall policies of the health care facility, taking into consideration the health needs of the community with a view toward elimination of redundant efforts.
- Provide adequate equipment necessary to fulfill the objectives and purposes of the health care facility.
- Ensure that the professional standards of health care personnel employed in the institution meet the minimal requirements of the federal, state, and municipal regulatory agencies.
- Receive reports from the administrator keeping them advised of financial, professional, and administrative aspects of the operation of the health care facility.

- Approve a budget submitted by the administrator to ensure the solvency of the health care facility.
- Ensure that all rules, regulations, and ordinances of federal, state, and municipal agencies are complied with and receive adequate reports regarding such compliance.
- Receive reports from the administrator regarding activities of the several departments within the facility.

Because the governing board is the ultimate authority in the facility, **procedures** must be established to:

- Make sure board members are aware of any statutory requirements regarding the incorporation and establishment of the health care facility.
- Provide reports from the administrator to keep members informed, in a general way, of all activities taking place in the organization.
- Remind board members to avoid self-dealing in any matter relating to the business of the corporation.
- Make sure any member's dissent from a board action is properly identified and in the board minutes.
- Remind members to attend the board meetings regularly.
- Ensure that members know the duties and responsibilities, rules and regulations, and bylaws of the health care facility.

LIABILITY INSURANCE FOR OFFICERS AND DIRECTORS

There has been a definite trend in the American corporate structure in recent years to sue board members and officers personally. However, this trend has not become prevalent in the health care field to date. Ordinarily, members of the board of directors of a nursing facility are immune from personal liability if they have not directly participated in an alleged negligent act of their agents or servants. The board of directors as a legal entity is usually sued and, if there is a recovery, it is from the board, not from the individual board members. Many nursing facilities carry liability insurance to protect the board members as a whole, should a judgment be rendered against them for their negligent acts or the negligent acts of their agents.

Several states have statutes that provide for a corporation to purchase and maintain insurance on behalf of individual directors, officers, employees, or agents of a corporation that protects them from any liability they may incur in any capacity arising from their board membership. The consensus seems to be that there is no public policy that forbids corporate directors and officers from being protected. Even though there has been little litigation against board officers or members and/or recovery from insurance companies, these policies are hard to place, generally. Coverage is available from companies including Lloyds of London, Pacific Indemnity Company in Los Angeles, American Home Assurance Company in New York, and St. Paul Fire and Marine, St. Paul, Minnesota. There are two major forms of directors and officers liability insurance.

Directors and Officers Policy

These policies generally provide that if, during the period of the policy, claims are made against the officers and directors who are insured for doing wrongful acts collectively or as individuals, the company pays on their behalf 95 percent of all loss that the insured may be legally obligated to pay. The payment is in accordance with the insured's agreement as to the amount of coverage. Usually, the policy also covers any loss arising against the estate, heirs, and legal representatives of those directors who were active in the corporation at the time of the wrongful act. When an insurance company writes a policy that uses such language as "legally obligated to pay," there must be proof that a legal obligation existed or that there was some fault on behalf of the insured in order to collect. The wrongful act of a director or officer of the corporation is not imputed to any other director or officer generally. There are many exclusions in the usual policy; common ones are:

- for intentional torts of libel or slander
- for those directors who use a corporation for personal gain or profit
- for those directors who are legally determined to have been dishonest
- where the directors and officers have other policies covering them for the same loss
- where the directors and officers are entitled to be indemnified by the corporation itself

Corporation Reimbursement Policy

Most of these policies provide that, during the policy period, the insurance company pays on behalf of the corporation 95 percent of all loss that the corporation may be required to pay to the directors or officers for claims made against them for individual or collective wrongful acts. Again, there is usually a clause covering the heirs, estates, and legal representatives of directors and officers who were directors and officers at the time of the wrongful act. The exclusions relate to each director and officer insured in this form of policy.

CHAPTER 7

Licensing of Nursing Facility Administrators

In 1970, an amendment to the Social Security Act (Section 1980 of Title XIX) required that all nursing facility administrators be licensed by July 1972 if the facility wished to participate in Medicaid. The law further required all states to pass enabling legislation creating an administrative body to ensure adherence with the federal requirements. The resulting state laws passed relative to the licensing of administrators, their background, educational requirements and licensing procedures, examinations, and renewals vary from state to state. Following are the general criteria addressed in this area of licensure.

STATE BOARD OF EXAMINERS

Each state passed enabling legislation (licensure statutes) so that the federal rules and regulations have legal effect within each state. The state statutes created the licensing board (board of examiners), which is an administrative agency with responsibility and authority specifically to provide the mechanism for handling licensure of nursing facility administrators. The enabling act defines the need for action by the state government, establishes general policy, and provides for appointment of a board with the necessary authority to promulgate rules and regulations to carry out its functions.

Once the guidelines are established by the enabling act, the details of operation are left to the administrative agency. Guidelines are set in place that outline the duties and responsibilities of the chairperson and secretary and establish other operational rules. Rules and regulations must be within the intent and scope of the statute that created them; if they are not, they are null and void. The legislative function of the licensing board is to impose requirements and to provide penalties for noncompliance. The adjudication function of the board involves interpretation of its own rules as to compliance and noncompliance and hearings to determine whether or not licenses will be granted, suspended, or revoked.

Licensing boards are administrative agencies and have limitations on the powers that are given to them, the greatest being that alleged violators have the right to appeal the administrative decisions to a court of law. One of the basic principles of the adjudication process is that the alleged violator is presumed innocent until guilt is determined. Reversals of decisions of the licensing board occur when a rule promulgated is not within its scope of authority or not related to the intent of the statute creating the agency.

Definitions generally used in state rules and regulations in this area are:

- **board**, meaning the state board of examiners of nursing facility administrators
- **nursing home/facility administrator**, meaning any individual who is charged with the general administration of a nursing facility, whether or not this individual has an ownership interest in the facility, and whether or not his or her functions and duties are shared with one or more individuals, and who has been licensed and registered as such by the board in accordance with the state licensing statute
- **administrator-in-training**, meaning an individual who is registered as such with the board pursuant to the law
- **practice of nursing facility administration**, meaning the performance of any act or the making of any decision involved in the planning, organizing, directing, and control of the operation of a nursing facility
- **nursing facility**, meaning a place authorized as such by the appropriate state licensing agency
- **person**, meaning an individual and not a corporation, firm, association, partnership, institution, public body, joint stock association, or any other group of individuals

Typically, under **general powers** granted to the licensing board under the state enabling act, the board shall:

- Exercise such powers as provided by the laws of the state concerning the licensing and registration of nursing facility administrators.
- Appoint members annually with the approval of an advisory council and the state governor.
- Remove any member of the board for misconduct, incapacity, incompetence, or neglect of duty after such member is given a written statement of the charges and an opportunity to be heard thereon, subject to review by the state governor.
- Make and publish such rules and regulations within its powers, if deemed necessary and proper for the execution and enforcement of the laws, rules, and regulations governing the licensing and registering of nursing facility administrators.
- Consider any matter relating to the licensing and registration of nursing facility administrators at the request of the advisory council.
- Submit to the advisory council any professional or technical matter relating to the licensing and registration of nursing facility administrators of a general (not pertaining to specific individuals) nature. The advisory council shall submit its recommendation in writing to the board within the time it directs.
- Exercise quasijudicial powers consistent with the law, including the power to issue subpoenas, compel attendance of witnesses, and administer oaths.

Adoption of Rules and Regulations

Generally speaking, a certain procedure must be followed before a rule or regulation of the board of examiners becomes valid, amended, or repealed and effective. Any interested person may petition the licensing board, requesting a change or amendment of a rule. The steps include:

1. The proposed rule or regulation is made available for public inspection.
2. A notice of hearing concerning the proposed adoption or amendment is provided.
3. All interested persons are given adequate notice and reasonable opportunity to submit data or arguments in favor of or against the adoption, amendment, or repeal of the rule or regulation.

4. A copy of the rule or regulation is filed with the secretary of state.
5. After these procedures are followed, the rule or regulation is legally effective within a certain time after the filing.

LICENSING

Only an individual who has qualified as a licensed and registered nursing facility administrator, holding a valid registration certificate, has the right to use the title (or any abbreviation thereof) *nursing home administrator*.

Administrator-in-Training (AIT) Programs

Many states require an AIT internship for the purpose of obtaining the practical training and experience required by the particular state. Such training includes assisting with the administrative activities of a facility in accordance with recognized preceptoral guidelines published by universities and professional societies. Candidates register with the state licensing board before starting an internship. Registration is approved if the internship is served in a long-term care facility administered by a nursing facility administrator who is certified or appointed as a preceptor. Generally, AITs file progress reports, signed by their preceptors, with their licensing boards on a quarterly or other basis. The requirement for internship may be waived for candidates with a master's degree in nursing facility administration or a related health administration field.

Application for Examination

Applicants or candidates for examination and qualification as nursing facility administrators apply in writing on forms provided by the state licensing board and furnish evidence that they have met the preexamination requirements. No person is permitted to take the licensing examination unless he or she meets state requirements. Generally, the requirements include evidence that the candidate is:

- over 18 years of age
- a citizen of the United States or has declared the intention of becoming a citizen

- of good moral character, requiring letters from individuals engaged in business or professional work as to the character of the candidate.

  A person who willfully conceals the fact that he or she was convicted of a felony or misdemeanor would most likely be denied a license on the basis of misrepresentation. Some states do allow a candidate to be licensed if he or she has been convicted of a felony or misdemeanor, requiring that:
  - a certificate of good conduct (or equivalent written document) from the board of parole be filed with the board of examiners if the candidate has been convicted of a felony, or
  - a certificate or letter of good conduct from the proper parole, probation, court, or police authorities be filed with the board of examiners if the candidate was convicted of a misdemeanor
- suitable and fit to be licensed and practice as a nursing home administrator, requiring evidence of:
  - absence of physical impairments to perform the duties of a nursing facility administrator, including good health and freedom from contagious disease. If there are physical defects, the board of examiners may investigate to determine whether or not the physical disability will prohibit the person from doing a good job. A license should not be denied unless a connection between physical impairment and the ability to perform the job can be established.
  - absence of any mental impairment likely to interfere with the performance of the duties of a nursing facility administrator. Psychological or aptitude testing should not be a major factor to disqualify a candidate. The board of examiners may seek professional consultation if members feel there may be a connection between an emotional problem and the ability to do a satisfactory job as administrator.
  - ability to understand and communicate the general and technical information necessary to the operation of the facility. This is usually presumed if the candidate passed the basic core knowledge examination.
  - ability to assume responsibilities for administration of a facility, evidenced by prior accredited activities and services that have been evaluated by the board of examiners
  - ability to relate the physical, psychological, spiritual, emotional, and social needs of people who are ill and/or elderly to the administration of the facility to meet these needs. Evaluations

during internships or aptitude testing, using the same standards, apply equally to all, with separate judgment of each candidate in the area of suitability.

- a high school graduate, has obtained an associate, bachelor's, or master's degree, has taken specific hours of state-approved courses in nursing facility administration and/or met experience requirements, and has participated in state-required administrator-in-training programs.

Examinations

All states require a national examination and most require a state oral or written examination.

State Examination

Each state sets its own criteria relating to required education and experience to enter and continue in the practice of nursing facility administration. The pass/fail score is based on the complexity of each examination. These examinations are offered two to four times throughout the year.

National Examination

The purpose of this examination is to ensure that nursing facility administrators entering the field have the basic knowledge and skills for competent management of long-term care facilities. The content of the examination is based on role delineation outlining the major areas of practice, work-related tasks, and skills. The National Board of Examiners of Long-Term Care Administrators (NAB) examination is administered by the state; results are reported to the state where the candidate plans to practice. There are approximately 150 multiple-choice questions or incomplete statements with four possible responses. Allotted time is a little less than four hours. The pass/fail score is based on the complexity of the exam.

Subjects for Examination

All courses of study for training or continuing education offered by an educational institution, association, professional society, or other organization for the purpose of qualifying candidates for licensure as nursing home administrators are registered with the state licensing board and certified in accordance with both state and federal requirements in order to qualify for federal financial participation. Certificates or other evidence are issued by the sponsor upon successful completion of approved studies.

All programs follow a prescribed core of knowledge. At present, five domains of practice are covered in the licensing examination.

1. **resident care management**: nursing services; social services; foods services; medical services; therapeutic, recreational, and activity programs; medical records program; pharmaceutical program; rehabilitation program
2. **personnel management**: communication; recruiting, training, evaluating, and retaining individuals; personnel policies; employee health and safety program
3. **financial management**: budgets, monitoring of fiscal performance, financial audit and reporting system
4. **environmental management**: maintaining and improving buildings, grounds, and equipment; environment for residents, staff, and visitors; safety programs; fire, disaster, and emergency programs
5. **governance and management**: policies and procedures for continuing compliance with directives of governing entities; monitoring of outcomes of all programs; policies and procedures of facility to ensure effectiveness; communication with residents, families, staff, volunteers, and governing entities to maximize resident's quality of life; integration of residents' rights with all aspects of the facility's operation; risk management program; information for residents and community about services offered; integration of the facility and other community resources, including educational institutions, hospitals, and vendors

LICENSES AND REGULATION

Licenses

A candidate for licensure as a nursing facility administrator who has successfully complied with the requirements of the state licensing laws and standards, passed the examinations, and complied with any required administrator-in-training program is issued a license certifying that he or she has met the requirements of the laws, rules, and regulations and is entitled to serve, act, and practice as a duly licensed nursing facility administrator. Licenses and certificates of registration are to be conspicuously displayed in the employment places of the licensees.

The board may issue a temporary license to any individual who has served as a nursing facility administrator during the calendar year preceding the application for the temporary license and meets the standards relating to good character, suitability, age, and citizenship. Such licenses are usually issued for six months, during which the administrator can build up an unmet experience or educational qualification or take the state examination.

Registration

State licensing boards maintain a register of all applications for licensing and registration of nursing facility administrators showing name, residence, place of employment, date of application, educational and experience qualifications, date and serial number of the license and registration certificates issued to the applicant, date on which the board reviewed and acted upon the application, and other pertinent information that the board deems necessary.

The certificate of registration is issued at the same time as the license. Annually or biennially, the nursing facility administrator must apply to the board, pay a registration fee, report any facts requested by the board on its forms, and submit evidence that he or she has attended continuing education programs in accordance with state law. A current certificate of registration is then issued by the board. An administrator failing to comply and continuing to practice as a nursing facility administrator may be suspended by the board.

Reciprocity

State licensing boards endorse nursing facility administrator licenses from other states upon submission of the application and payment of a fee. Although there are many variations, states basically require that:

- The other state's system and standards of qualification are substantially equivalent to those of the state being applied to.
- The applicant meets these educational and experience standards currently or at the time of issuance of the previous license.

- The applicant has passed the national exam.
- The applicant holds a valid nursing facility administrator's license and has practiced as a nursing facility administrator within a certain period.
- The applicant is familiar with the state's local and state-related health and safety regulations. Some states require that a written or oral examination be taken and passed.
- The applicant's state gives similar recognition to any nursing facility administrators' licenses from the state being applied to.

Exhibit 7–1 shows a sample reciprocity agreement.

REFUSAL, SUSPENSION, AND REVOCATION OF LICENSES

The practice of nursing facility administration is an important property right. To operate a business and work as a nursing home administrator is fully protected by the United States Constitution and the Fifth and Fourteenth Amendments in the due process clause. A license cannot be arbitrarily revoked or suspended, thereby denying practice as a nursing home administrator. Many states have statutes and procedures that guarantee basic rights of due notice and formal hearing, should a license be suspended or revoked. If an administrative hearing within the structure of the licensing board renders an adverse decision, appeal is ensured by law to the state court for a complete hearing. Legal counsel helps to fully protect rights during each step of an administrative hearing or an appeal.

The licensing board may reprimand or otherwise discipline any permanent or provisional licensee or administrator-in-training upon substantial evidence that the individual is:

- incompetent to engage in the practice of nursing facility administration
- a habitual drunkard
- addicted to or dependent on the use of morphine, opium, cocaine, or other drugs having an abnormal effect

The licensing board may suspend, revoke, or refuse to issue a license to a nursing facility administrator, administrator-in-training, or provisional licensee if the individual has:

- Violated any provisions of the law pertaining to the licensing of nursing facility administrators.
- Willfully or repeatedly violated any of the provisions of the law, code, rules, or regulations of the licensing board.
- Been convicted of a crime.
- Practiced fraud, deceit, or misrepresentation in securing a nursing facility administrator's license or in his or her capacity as a nursing facility administrator.
- Practiced without registration.
- Temporarily or permanently transferred his or her license or certificate to any other person wrongfully.
- Paid, given, caused to be paid or given, or offered to pay or give a commission or other valuable consideration to any person for the solicitation or procurement for facility patronage.
- Been guilty of fraudulent, misleading, or deceptive advertising.
- Falsely impersonated another licensee.
- Failed to exercise true regard for the safety, health, and life of residents.
- Willfully permitted unauthorized disclosure of information relating to a resident or his or her records.
- Discriminated in respect to residents, employees, or staff on account of race, religion, color, or national origin.

Any administrator or administrator-in-training convicted of a felony must forfeit his or her license and registration when the licensing board receives a certified copy of the court record indicating this individual's felony conviction.

COMPLAINTS AND HEARING PROCEDURES

Any person, public officer, association, or the licensing board may prefer charges against a permanent or temporary licensee or administrator-in-training for due cause, with the charges submitted to the board in writing.

Licensing Board Procedure

The board holds a preliminary hearing to determine if action is warranted. If not, the charges and an order to dismiss the charges are filed with the board; if so, the board designates a hearing officer to determine the charges, set a time and place for the hearing, and serve a copy of the charges and notice of the hearing to the accused by mail or newspaper publication at least 10 days before the hearing date. After the hearing, the board may revoke or suspend (with or without provision for reinstatement) a license, reprimand or take other disciplinary action, dismiss the action, or direct a rehearing and take additional evidence to confirm or rescind the prior determination. A revoked license may be restored at the discretion of the board when satisfactory evidence has been submitted that the disability has been removed; there may be a formal hearing on the matter.

Hearings

The conduct of administrative hearings is usually spelled out in the statutes relative to administrative boards. The main parts covering the rights and obligations of the parties are, generally, as follows. Any party to hearings may appear personally with counsel and must be given opportunity to produce evidence and witnesses on his or her behalf and to cross-examine witnesses. Hearing officers must advise the parties that these are their rights, with all appearances noted in the official records of the hearing. The hearing officer may issue subpoenas or subpoenas duces tecum or grant adjournment until a designated date at the prior written request of any party. While the hearing officer is not bound by rules of evidence in the conduct of the hearing, any determination and recommendations must be founded on sufficient legal evidence to sustain the decision. At the conclusion of the hearing, the board takes action by written order, including any civil penalties provided by law, based on the written findings and determination. The record, minutes, and evidence of a formal hearing are made available to all parties for examination.

Remedies

A nursing facility administrator may have the following remedies, should the licensing board deny or refuse to renew his or her license. The related laws vary in each state.

- All parties (licensing board and aggrieved party) are afforded an opportunity for a hearing after a reasonable notice.

- The notice of the hearing includes a clear and concise statement of the issue involved, reference to the rules and statutes involved, outline of the legal authority and jurisdiction under which the hearing will be held, and time and place the hearing is scheduled.
- The aggrieved party may respond and present evidence supporting his or her claim, preferably through an attorney.
- The aggrieved party may request a written copy of any adverse decision, stating the reasons for it.
- Providing timely application was made for licensure renewal, if denied, the existing license will not expire until any contest has been terminated.
- A license may be immediately revoked if the licensing board states in writing in the order that the health, safety, or welfare of residents requires emergency action.
- The aggrieved party may appeal to state courts after all administrative remedies have been exhausted. His or her attorney files a petition for review of the licensing board's decision within the time limit (usually 30 days after the notice of the final decision is mailed). The court may modify, reverse, or order a review of the licensing board's decision after finding there was:
  - an exceeding of the licensing board's authority
  - a procedural error
  - an error of law
  - insufficient evidence
  - arbitrary, capricious, or unwarranted exercise of discretion on the part of the licensing board
- Timely petition to the appellate or supreme state court may be made if the decision is still adverse.

Exhibit 7–1 Sample Reciprocity Agreement

(Established by the National Association of Boards of Examiners for Nursing Home Administrators)

INTERSTATE COMPACT FOR RECIPROCITY OR ENDORSEMENT OF LICENSURE FOR NURSING HOME ADMINISTRATORS

For and Between the States of _____ and _____

Whereas the undersigned represent that they are the duly designated representatives of the licensure authorities for the licensing of nursing home administrators of the respective states or territories signatory hereto; and

Whereas it is the desire and intent of the said licensure authorities to provide, establish, and effect reciprocal licensure or endorsement of nursing home administrator licenses issued to licensees of the state or territories signatory hereto;

Now, therefore, it is hereby stipulated, consented to, and agreed:

1. That the licensing laws, rules and regulations, requirements, and standards in respect to and controlling the licensing, registration, and regulation of nursing home administrators in their respective states or territories are substantially equal.
2. That the states or territories signatory hereto, in consideration for their acknowledgment, of the substantial equality of licensing and registration standards aforesaid, will recognize and accept for reciprocal licensure purposes the license of any person duly licensed and registered by the states or territories signatory hereto, as a nursing home administrator, subject to the following provisions. That:
   a. The applicant for such reciprocal licensure or endorsement shall make formal application for such licensure or endorsement on forms provided therefor and by the state or territory to which application for such licensing or endorsement is made, and is required by law in effect at the time of such application.
   b. This compact shall be construed to apply for such licensing or endorsement only to nursing home administrators who obtain a nursing home administrator's license through recognized written examination and who have actively engaged in the practice of nursing home administration as a licensed and registered nursing home administrator in the state or territory on whose license they apply, preceding the filing of an application for reciprocity or endorsement.

continues

Exhibit 7–1 continued

    c. Each state or territory signatory hereto, in its discretion, may require an applicant for such licensing or endorsement to pass a written examination pertaining to the laws and regulations relating to the practice of nursing home administration in effect in the state or territory to which the applicant is applying for such licensure or endorsement.

    d. The licensing laws, rules and regulations, requirements, and standards in respect to and controlling the licensing, registration, and regulation of nursing home administrators in their respective states or territories are substantially equal at the time that application for such reciprocal licensing or endorsement is made.

    e. The state or territory signatory hereto does not waive its legal responsibility for evaluating the applicant in total.

    f. The state or territory signatory hereto agrees to mutually furnish a total exchange of information relative to the applicant.

3. This compact may be canceled at any time by a state or territory signatory hereto by giving written notice that on or after a date specified in such notice the compact will be deemed terminated and canceled.

State Boards of Nursing Home Administrators:

State of _____

Dated: _____

By: _____ , Chairperson

By: _____ , Secretary

State of _____

Dated: _____

By: _____ , Chairperson

By: _____ , Secretary

CHAPTER 8

Authority, Functions, and Liability of the Administrator

AUTHORITY AND FUNCTIONS OF THE ADMINISTRATOR

A nursing home administrator is a licensed professional specifically trained for this position. Administrators are held to standards of professional competence in the same manner as are nurses, pharmacists, and other professional paramedical licensed personnel who are hired to provide a direct service.

The administrator is hired to manage the facility and must meet certain standards of professional conduct. He or she is the chief executive officer and legally has the responsibility for all activities in the facility, but often delegates some of this authority. The administrator is responsible for a broad spectrum of activities involving not only the internal operation of the facility but external activities in the community. The ownership or corporate board of directors of the facility retains the ultimate legal responsibility. If the administrator fails to meet the duties and obligations within standards of professional conduct, any resulting liability could be imputed to him or her personally or to his or her employer.

Administrator and Governing Board

The governing body has the ultimate legal responsibility for the management of the long-term care facility and must, therefore, establish policies and be kept informed of activities within it. The board may guide the administrator in a general way, but being successful businesspersons and leaders in the community does not necessarily qualify them as experts in the health care field; the administrator must be the expert. A voluntary board of citizens does not have a great deal of time to devote to the operational details of a health care facility and, out of necessity, must delegate sufficient authority to the administrator to carry out the legal responsibility of these operations. Although the governing board must delegate authority to the administrator, he or she remains accountable to the board. The administrator is not the business manager but the overall supervisor of all functions, both administrative and medico-administrative. The administrator should assist the board in establishing general policy, which it is up to the administrator to implement. He or she should attend all meetings of the governing board and its committees.

The trend today is to put the administrator on the same level as other board members. In private corporations, the president of the corporation is a member of the board but not necessarily the chairperson of the board. The administrator, as a board member, should not vote on any matter that concerns him or her personally (employment contract, fringe benefits, etc.), as courts may hold that this is a conflict of interest.

The relationship of the administrator to the governing board or ownership is one of employer-employee and principal-agent. As an employee, the administrator carries out the duties prescribed by the governing body; as an agent, the governing body vests part of its authority in the administrator. The proportion of these legal relationships depends on the employment contract.

Employer-Employee Relationship

As an employee, the administrator holds the same legal relationship to the employer as the other employees do and is concerned with the relationships within the facility. His or her immediate supervisor, however, is not one person but the total board of directors.

Principal-Agent Relationship

The principal-agent relationship is contractual and based on mutual consent (employment contract) between the administrator and the governing board, whereby the administrator represents the governing body in dealings with third parties (e.g., insurers, vendors, contractors) to manage affairs or perform some service. The administrator has power to act only in accordance with the authority granted by the principals or owners of the nursing facility. As an agent, the administrator receives actual authority, apparent authority, or inherent power to act for the ownership.

- **Actual authority** refers to the power the administrator has to do certain acts allowed by the ownership (principal) to carry out the objectives of the nursing facility. This authority stems from the job description of the administrator, which may be included in the constitution and bylaws of the corporation or as a written document in the employment contract. If an administrator has actual authority, he or she also has incidental authority to carry out the task. Actual authority may be given by the ownership in writing, orally, or by implication from the circumstances of a particular situation. Actual authority is given by implication, depending upon the intent of the principal to confer the authority or to cause the administrator to believe that he or she has the authority.

  For example, when the principal instructs the administrator to negotiate with the welfare department or another third-party payer, the administrator may have authority to carry out all the necessary steps in concluding a contractual relationship for the nursing facility.

- **Apparent authority** comes about if the ownership leads a third party to believe that the administrator has the authority to perform a certain task. The expression of authority is made to a third party with whom the administrator deals rather than directly to the administrator, as with actual authority.

  For example, the ownership sends a letter to the welfare department or Blue Cross directly, stating that the administrator is the representative of the facility relative to the negotiation of a contract; the ownership has given the administrator apparent authority because the representation was made by the ownership to a third party rather than to the administrator directly.

- **Inherent authority** is power that the administrator has by the fact he or she is the agent of the facility. It is not connected with any express or implied grant of authority from the principal. The courts recognize this kind of authority when it is necessary to protect third persons with whom the administrator may be dealing.

  For example, a nursing facility employs an administrator to function as its general manager and directs him to purchase all of its supplies from a certain vendor. The administrator violates these instructions and purchases supplies from another vendor, who is not aware of the special instructions previously given to the administrator. Ordinarily, the administrator has inherent authority, by virtue of his position as administrator, to purchase from any vendor, and the ownership is bound by the transaction; this inherent authority is recognized by law to protect the innocent vendor. In this example, there is no actual authority because the administrator violated his express instructions, and there is no apparent authority because the principal made no representations to the third party regarding the administrator's authority in this matter. The administrator could be held personally liable for the amount paid and possibly lose his job for violating instructions.

An act formerly completed by the administrator without authority can be affirmed or ratified by the owners or principal, thus authorizing the prior unauthorized act. For example, the job description of an administrator limits his purchase of new equipment to $1,500. An emergency occurs and the administrator feels he must act quickly, so he orders a piece of equipment that costs $2,000, thereby exceeding his authority. At the next meeting of the ownership, a resolution or verbal affirmation is made regarding the $2,000 purchase and the unauthorized act of the administrator now becomes an authorized act of the nursing facility. If the unauthorized act is not ratified, the administrator could be held personally liable for the additional costs.

To affirm or effectively ratify an administrator's unauthorized act, the owners of the facility must have knowledge of all the material facts involved in the act. The following actions constitute ratification by the principal or owners of a nursing facility for unauthorized acts of the administrator:

- **Conduct**, whereby the owners do something that expresses their intent to ratify.
- **Express affirmation**, whereby the owners expressly affirm a prior unauthorized act.
- **Implied affirmation**, whereby the owners' action authorizes the act. For example, in buying a supply of drugs at a special reduced price, the administrator exceeded his authority. If the facility retains the drugs and voluntarily accepts the benefits of this special purchase, the owners are deemed to have affirmed the unauthorized act of the administrator.

- **Failure to act**, whereby the owners' failure to revoke an unauthorized act may constitute affirmation. For example, an administrator spends $1,000 in a large urban area to get nurses for the facility, exceeding his express authority to spend only $500 for such purposes. The owners learn of this and realize that the advertising agency is spending their time and money in preparation of the copy and do nothing to repudiate the order. A court would most likely hold that the failure to act and knowledge of all material facts amounts to affirmation of the administrator's act.

Code of Ethics

High standards of integrity and ethical principles are an essential part of the professional responsibilities of long-term health care administration. The American College of Health Care Administrators (ACHCA) promulgated the following fundamental rules as basic to carrying out this responsibility.

The welfare of persons for whom care is provided is predominant. In support of this, the administrator needs to:

- Provide the highest quality of appropriate services possible in light of available resources.
- Comply with laws, regulations, and standards of recognized practice in the operation of the facility.
- Protect each resident's confidentiality of information.
- Conduct administrative duties with personal integrity, earning confidence, trust, and respect in the community.
- Avoid any illegal discriminatory actions that are not related to the bona fide requirements of quality care.
- Maintain the confidentiality of professional or personal information regarding residents to unauthorized personnel unless required by law or to protect the public welfare.

The administrator must maintain high standards of professional competence and must:

- Possess and maintain the competencies that are necessary to effectively carry out his or her responsibilities.

- Practice administration in accordance with his or her capabilities and seek counsel from other qualified persons when appropriate.
- Obtain continuing education and professional development.
- Accurately represent qualifications, education, experience, and affiliations.
- Provide other services than those for which he or she is prepared and qualified.

In his or her practice of long-term care administration, the administrator must strive to maintain professionalism, placing the interest of the facility and its residents first, and shall:

- Avoid partisanship, providing a forum for the fair resolution of disputes involving the management of the facility or delivery of services.
- Disclose to the governing body or other appropriate authorities any circumstances concerning him or her that might create conflict of interest or have a substantial adverse impact on the facility or its residents.
- Refrain from participating in any activity that might create a conflict of interest or have a substantial adverse impact on the facility or its residents.

Long-term care administrators also honor their responsibilities to the public, their profession, and the relationships with colleagues and members of related professions. In this area, they:

- Foster increased knowledge and support research efforts within their profession.
- Participate in community planning to provide a full range of health care services.
- Share their expertise with colleagues, students, and the public to promote understanding of long-term health care.
- Inform the ACHCA Standards and Ethics Committee of violations of their code of ethics and cooperate with related sanctioned inquiries.
- Must not defend, support, or ignore any unethical conduct of colleagues, peers, or students.

Exhibit 8–1 shows a sample job description for an administrator.

Exhibit 8–1 Sample Job Description—Administrator

The administrator shall exercise general management of the nursing facility.

The administrator shall provide for the implementation of policies, directives, and resolutions promulgated by the governing body.

The administrator shall see to it that the rules and regulations of the state board of health and other regulatory agencies are complied with regarding the operation of the health care facility.

The administrator shall develop, maintain, and administer a sound plan of organization.

The administrator shall be responsible for maintaining high standards of resident care.

The administrator shall maintain the nursing facility in a solvent condition and make such recommendations to the board of directors as necessary to the attainment of this objective. The administrator is responsible for the supervision and preparation of the annual budget.

With regard to expenditures of capital nature, the administrator is granted the authority to present for approval of the governing board requests for new and replacement of existing equipment not included in the annual budget in amounts over $1,500.

The approval of the governing board is necessary for plans and procedures involving major structural changes of the physical plant; for major personnel policies and wage and salary programs; for plans and procedures to introduce, expand, or delete health services; for major changes in rates and charges for services and raising additional income from sources outside operating income; for initial contractual agreements regarding third-party payers; and for creation of new positions, new departments, and new educational programs.

The administrator shall arrange a contract agreement with the medical director regarding the duties, responsibilities, and compensation of this position. He or she shall supervise medico-administrative decisions in relation to federal and state regulations and facility policies concerning physician and medical director responsibilities in the facility and ensure their implementation.

In regard to relations with other health care facilities, the administrator shall develop a working relationship with third-party payers and negotiate contractual agreements, subject to approval of the board of directors; cooperate with other health care agencies so that the health services of the

continues

Exhibit 8–1 continued

> community are coordinated; and develop and maintain a favorable image of the health care facility by keeping the public informed through cooperation with the news media.
>
> The administrator shall report regularly to the governing body and submit an annual report on the operation of the health care facility.
>
> The duties of the administrator at any time may be assigned by the governing body.

Administrators' Traits

Desirable traits of an administrator include these:

- **Have tact and diplomacy.** The administrator is constantly working with many types of people. He or she may work with a sick resident or with a doctor, plan a project with the auxiliary, or discuss the institution with a lawyer or businessperson.
- **Be firm** and able to make a decision when it is required. The most ineffective administrator is one who sits on the fence on all issues and refuses to make a decision for fear he or she may upset someone. There are times when a decision must be made and it is up to the administrator to make it.
- **Spend a great deal of time** organizing the facility as its chief executive officer. It is impossible to have an efficiently operating facility unless departments are properly organized and lines of communication are established within the organizational structure.
- **Be a leader** in the health care facility and in the community. The administrator should know how to work with people and develop confidence in them. Leadership cannot be legislated. It must be shown by the administrator's actions on a daily basis.
- **Maintain high principles** and be impartial in working with physicians, personnel, and other individuals in the health care field. He or she must have the administrative courage to adhere to principles.
- **Like the work.** The administrator is technically on the job 24 hours a day and should take a personal interest in the work.
- **Have administrative ability** to coordinate the activities of others. In the larger facility, he or she will delegate much of the administrative

authority to highly qualified department heads. In the smaller facility, the administrator may be performing the functions of many job titles.

- **Appear neat and tidy.** The administrator should set a good example for others in the health care facility.
- **Have the ability to communicate** both orally and in writing. Therefore, a command of the English language is important.
- **Be able to analyze fact situations**, to separate unnecessary verbiage, and to present ideas in a concrete form.
- **Like to read** and keep up with the current literature in the field.
- **Be imaginative** and innovative in the health care field.
- **Have empathy** and like to work with older people.

Administrator's Duties within the Facility

The administrator is the liaison officer of the board of directors, the organized medical staff (if there is one), and the department heads in the health facility. He or she must communicate policy to the members of the general staff. The number of organized departments varies with the size of the facility but the functions that must be performed do not. Whether the facility is large or small, the following functions must be performed: bookkeeping and accounting, personnel, dietary, housekeeping, laundry, pharmacy, and resident care.

Relative to Reports

Communications between the board of directors and the administrator are important. One way in which the administrator may communicate effectively with the board is to present monthly reports to the board. An agenda for board meetings should be prepared by the administrator and distributed to the board before the meeting. When several items require statistical documentation, the agenda should be distributed to the members before the meeting so they have the opportunity to study the material and prepare questions to ask at the meeting. Monthly profit and loss statements should be prepared and discussed at the meetings. The business manager may prepare the report but the administrator presents the report to the board. Some health care facilities invite the business manager to attend the meetings of the board to address any details about the preparation of the report. However, the responsibility for reporting still is with the administrator. He or she should study a problem, do the detail groundwork in gathering statistics to present, and make an appropriate recommendation to the board, which may or may not accept the recommendation.

Relative to Personnel

The administrator has obligations relative to the hiring, supervision, and retention of all personnel in the facility and must see that a policy is in place and followed. As he or she does not personally hire each person, a mechanism should be established to receive important information regarding all employees and their activities.

The selection of department heads should be made by the administrator. Because these individuals are the key to the successful operation of the long-term care facility, the administrator must have a good working relationship with them. All department heads report to the administrator. In large facilities, very often, an assistant administrator coordinates the activities of some of the departments and then reports to the administrator.

The administrator is responsible for the training of personnel concerning the mission, rules, and regulations of the facility and for keeping employee morale high. In a smaller facility, he or she may be responsible for establishing and implementing personnel practices that are equitable and just. In the larger institution, a personnel manager may assist the administrator in carrying out this function.

Relative to Quality of Care

The landmark case of *Darling v. Charlestown Community Hospital*, 211 NE 2nd 253, established a duty for the administrator to be involved in the quality of care rendered in the facility. The Omnibus Budget Reconciliation Act (OBRA) of 1987 mandates that the facility have operational a quality assessment and assurance program and a committee to monitor the quality of services in all areas. All providers must meet the provisions of a quality assurance program that stresses health outcomes and provides data to measure these outcomes and other indicators of quality.

The nursing home administrator coordinates resident care management and must be able to plan, implement, and evaluate the care program. He or she needs broad knowledge in the areas of the needs of those coming into the facility for care, the roles and standards of the personnel (nurses, aides, dietitians, social workers, etc.) caring for the residents, and all applicable standards, rules, regulations, and new legislation to make sure that the facility is in compliance. A breach of federal or state standards is an important consideration in determining what standard of care should apply in negligence actions.

Relative to the Medical Director

Most nursing facilities do not have an organized medical staff. However, the governing body, through its medical director, must monitor physicians to see that all regulations regarding physicians with patients in a nursing facility are being complied with. The medico-administrative decisions with respect to these regulations are part of the responsibility of the administrator.

The medical director of a nursing facility is usually a full- or part-time physician. Some of his or her duties are to implement and enforce the policies relative to medical care in the facility as required by federal and state law. The Code of Federal Regulations, Part 42, 430 to end, 10-1-98, requires nursing facilities to ensure that:

- A physician must personally approve in writing a recommendation for an individual to be admitted to a facility.
- Each resident is under the care of a physician.
- Another physician supervises the medical care of a resident when the attending physician is unavailable.

In most cases, the legal status of an attending physician in a nursing facility is one of independent contractor. This means that any negligence caused by the attending physician is not imputed to the nursing facility under respondeat superior because the medical director is not an employee of the facility relative to medical care. (However, some large corporate facilities do employ a physician as medical director.)

The administrator should be involved in, and supervise, the medical director's contractual agreements with the facility regarding the director's duties, responsibilities, and compensation. The administrator should also ensure that the rules are adhered to regarding physician visits, frequency of physician visits, availability of physicians for emergency care, and proper physician delegation of tasks to be performed by a nurse practitioner, clinical nurse specialist, or physician's assistant who is not an employee of the facility but who is working in collaboration with the physician.

Relative to the Nursing Service

The primary role of the nursing department in the facility is the proper care of the residents. The administrator is responsible for the selection of the director of nursing and has authority to both employ and discharge him or her. Because of the importance of this position in the facility, it would probably be judicious for the administrator to consult with the board before any action is taken.

The administrator delegates some of his or her authority to the director of nursing to operate the nursing department. Since he or she retains the legal responsibility for the operation of the entire facility, mechanisms for receiving reports and communications from the director of nursing should be established.

Relative to the Dietary Department

Generally, the administrator monitors food preparation and delivery for therapeutic and individual satisfaction in accordance with resident care plans. He or she must see that sanitation levels are maintained and regulations met in this area.

The food service of a health facility is an important factor in therapy and the quality of life of the resident and in maintaining good public relations with the community. The resident judges the quality of the health care facility by the type of nursing service rendered, the cleanliness of the facility, and the food served. If the food is therapeutically good for the resident, is hot when received by the resident, and is attractively served, the image regarding food service should be good.

A qualified dietitian should be on the dietary staff full-time or on a consulting basis. The administrator is responsible for retaining the dietitian, who reports directly to him or her. The purchasing of food for the facility is often done by the dietitian.

Relative to Fiscal Solvency

The administrator is responsible for the fiscal solvency of the health care institution. To carry out this responsibility, he or she should prepare or have prepared an annual budget for submission to the governing body for approval. This budget includes salary projections, supply and expense projections, and equipment projections. A personnel department may assist the administrator in obtaining information for the establishment of a wage and salary program; the administrator should be empowered to fix all salaries within the limits of the budget.

If the facility has a comptroller or a business manager, he or she should be given the responsibility of doing the actual detail work on the budget, to be reviewed and approved by the administrator before he or she submits it to the board for approval. Once the budget is approved, the administrator should operate the health care facility within its guidelines.

Relative to Risk Management

Risk management is a program to anticipate possible legal problems and to manage or reduce them. Identification of risks is a first step in such a program. Generally, risks fall into two categories:

1. **Physical risks**, which include such physical plant concerns as fire safety, disaster, emergency procedures, and all of the standards (Life Safety Code, American Standards for the Physically Handicapped, American Disabilities Act, etc.) that the facility must meet in order to be licensed, certified, or accredited.
2. **Resident care risks**, which include poor policies and procedures relating to the resident care, such as poor recordkeeping, ignoring residents' rights, improper use of restraints, poor medication procedures, and negligence in keeping records of incidents that take place in the facility. Lack of preemployment tests for screening new employees also falls into this category.

Some steps that can be taken to reduce occurrences that may lead to legal liability are:

1. Make certain the facility has adequate insurance coverage to cover the risks that may be incurred.
2. Document all incidents and accidents that occur in the facility.
3. Provide good inservice training for employees.
4. Maintain an active quality assessment and assurance committee.

Relative to the Business Office

The lifeblood of any health care facility, whether it be incorporated as a for-profit or nonprofit facility, is the ability to generate income and to keep the operation solvent. The administrator must work closely with the office manager regarding fiscal operations. With the advent of third-party payers, most health facilities are financed primarily by insurance policies (private insurance companies, Blue Cross, Medicare, and Medicaid) held by residents, either on a group or an individual basis. It is, therefore, important that the administrator be familiar with the concept of reimbursement, the legislative requirements of Medicare and Medicaid, and the total insurance process as it relates to the health care facility. Unless he or she has special training in this area, the administrator is not expected to do the accounting for the facility. However, he or she should be familiar with accounting statements so as to properly interpret and analyze a profit and loss statement and a balance sheet and to be conversant with procedures relating to accounts payable and accounts receivable within the organization.

Relative to the Purchasing Function

The administrator has certain responsibilities as an agent for the facility to make sure proper purchasing procedures are established. One responsibility is to protect the assets of the corporation; in order to do so adequately, good procedures must be established and implemented. Larger facilities have a purchasing agent who does all the ordering for the facility, with the exception of food, in coordination with the administrator and department heads. In others, this is combined with another function. Consortiums may be formed with other health care providers in the geographic area to achieve greater economy in the purchase of services and supplies.

Relative to the Physical Environment

The administrator needs to have broad knowledge of the state and federal regulations applicable to the physical environment (National Fire Protection Association, Americans with Disabilities Act, American National Standards Institute, Occupational Safety and Health Act) to ensure the facility's compliance and to protect its residents and others coming into the facility. An infection control committee must be operational to prevent, control, and monitor contagious disease and infections and to ensure the use of universal precaution measures. Equipment used by residents must meet their needs and be on a preventive maintenance program. Disaster and fire preparedness programs must be established and operational.

Generally, the housekeeper is responsible for the cleanliness of the facility and the maintenance engineer is responsible for all other physical aspects of the operation. These department heads report to the administrator and keep him or her informed of any significant related problems. Because of possible negligence on the part of the facility, it is important that the administrator be informed immediately of any defects in operating equipment, on the grounds, or in the building.

Administrator's Duties outside the Facility

Relative to the Health Field

The duties of the administrator should not be limited to activities within the walls of the building. Nursing facilities are an integral part of the community. From the view of health care planning, it is important that all health care providers and hospitals work together and cooperate with each other when possible. The administrator of a health care facility should be active in local, state, and national health organizations, such as the local nursing facility council, state association, the American Health Care Association, and ACHCA. By keeping active in the health field, he or she stays abreast of the many changes taking place in a dynamic area of management.

Relative to the Community

The administrator is considered a leader in the community and his or her actions are often interpreted as representative of the health care facility. He or she may be active in the community, joining a service club or participating on the boards of creditable organizations if requested to do so. As part of the public and community relations program, he or she may tell the story of the facility to the community by presenting talks to service clubs.

The public image of health care facilities has historically been poor. It appears that part of this poor image is due to lack of disclosure of information regarding the finances of the institution, the adequacy of the accommodations, whether the facility is approved by the accrediting agencies, and so on. Therefore, it is imperative that the administrator have a good working relationship with members of the press because of the help they can give in presenting favorable information (new personnel employed, new techniques or equipment used, special resident activities) to the community.

TORT LIABILITY OF THE ADMINISTRATOR

In the areas of civil and criminal law, an administrator or operator of a long-term care facility may hold the facility liable under respondeat superior or be held personally liable for his or her negligent and willful acts. The causal relationship between an alleged act and the injury of another must be established before liability is incurred.

There are three areas of possible tort liability to be considered.

1. negligent actions under the fault concept
2. negligent or willful acts as an agent
3. breach of a criminal or civil legal duty imposed by statute or regulations

Fault Concept of Negligence

Under general liability principles, fault is a breach of duty imposed by law or contract. To determine if the facility is liable or if the administrator is personally liable, the courts closely analyze the legal relationship that exists under the fault concept. If the administrator is considered to be an employee, his or her negligent acts are imputed to the facility, just as if the administrator were any other employee working within the scope of his or her employment.

The case of *Terrel v. Cockrell*, 286 SW 2d 950, questioned this relationship to determine liability. A hospital contracted with a physician to operate and manage its facilities. With the approval of the board of directors, the physician/administrator was appointed as its "general representative to supervise, direct, operate, and manage the hospital and all of its property," thus giving him full, complete, and sole power to manage the facility subject to the bylaws and charter. The physician/administrator was paid a monthly salary for his administrative responsibilities. He was also given space in the hospital without charge to operate a lab and X-ray as a private business.

A patient was admitted to the hospital, sedated, and placed in a bed. Hospital policy required that when patients were sedated, they were not to be left alone without the side rails up. An attendant left the side rails down and left the bedside. The patient fell out of bed and injured herself. The issue of who was liable depended on the legal relationship of the administrator to the hospital.

To function, the hospital must utilize agents and employees. Although the physician/administrator had the right to hire, fire, and supervise employees, they were employed by the hospital, which retains the right of supervision and control of the employees should it discharge the physician as administrator. Generally, where an employee under the authority of his or her employer engages another to perform work for the benefit of that employer, the employer (principal) is, in law, the master of the servant so engaged.

In this case, the court held that the attendant was the agent, servant, and employee of the hospital (not the administrator); the relationship between the hospital and administrator was determined also to be one of employer-employee, where the administrator would not be personally liable for negligent acts of the employees. If the attendant had been doing a negligent act involving the lab or X-ray, the negligence could have become the personal liability of the administrator, as the lab and X-ray were considered his private venture, where the theory of respondeat superior would not apply to the hospital but to the physician.

In *Hipp v. Hospital Authority of the City of Marietta*, 121 SE 273, the court considered whether the selection of employees is part of an administrator's duties. If so, was the administrator grossly negligent in failing to check references or failing to have an established policy for checking references and therefore personally liable? The court discussed the responsibility of a hospital and its agents relative to the selection of nonprofessional employees to work in the facility.

This was an action to recover damages resulting from an orderly molesting a nine-year-old patient, who charged the hospital with negligence concerning the selection and supervision of the orderly. It was alleged that the hospital had not investigated the moral character and background of the orderly; records indicated that the orderly had been convicted as a peeping Tom.

The court discussed the general law as to liability of the hospital should a servant deviate from his or her master's business to act outside of the job duties. The employee is considered on a "frolic of his or her own" and is liable for his or her actions personally in situations where the employer has no reason to anticipate such action and is not required to first determine the employee's competency when it comes to dealing with the public. The obligation of a proprietor to protect patrons from injury or mistreatment includes the duty to select and retain employees who are suitable to look after the safety and comfort of these patrons. This principle applies to a hospital where patients are confined to bed, wearing less clothes than in daily life, and under the control of the institution and its employees. The supervision of employees by those responsible for the protection of patients is a duty incumbent upon a professional person. An administrator could be held personally liable for lack of supervision of employees under his or her direct control if it is shown that he or she personally acted negligently and that these acts were the direct cause of injury to the patient.

Liability as an Agent

The administrator may be involved in a contractual relationship with a facility where the concept of principal-agent relationship comes into play, the principal being the facility and the agent being the administrator. This contractual relationship is the result of mutual consent and agreement in the form of an oral, written, express, or implied contract whereby the agent represents the principal in dealing with third parties when performing some service or in managing the affairs of the facility. The agent is subject to the orders and control of the principal, who has the right to discharge the agent for disobedience or misconduct. As an agent of the nursing facility, the administrator has certain duties and responsibilities to his or her principal. If these duties are breached by the administrator, exceeding his or her authority with third parties, the administrator may be held personally liable for his or her actions.

For example, an administrator has authority to enter into a contract with third parties to buy certain equipment for the facility and is authorized to purchase items not to exceed $5,000. The administrator buys an item for the facility costing $10,000, exceeding his or her authority. The administrator could be held personally liable for the item purchased without authority of the principal. If, however, the board of the facility agrees to pay for the item costing $10,000, the board is said to have ratified the act of the administrator, and he or she may not be liable.

Another area of possible personal liability of the administrator is when the administrator, as an agent of the facility, uses subagents to perform certain tasks, and the subagents are negligent. This negligence may be imputed to the administrator personally and not to the facility.

Breach of a Criminal or Civil Legal Duty Imposed by Statute or Regulation

Most states, in their licensing acts, describe the qualifications of the administrator. If an administrator works for a private ownership, a partnership, or a corporation, and his or her duties are described in the constitution and bylaws, the articles of partnership, or the articles of incorporation, he or she may be held personally liable should he or she willfully breach the specified duties.

A nursing home administrator may be held personally liable when he or she fails to perform acts required by his or her position as a professional or by law. Failure to attend to changes recommended by the Public Health Department following a facility inspection, failure to adhere to state safety codes, and failure to adhere to Medicare and Medicaid rules and regulations are all areas where an administrator could be held personally liable. If such malfeasance results in death or severe injury to a resident or involves self-dealing fraudulent schemes of embezzlement, the administrator could be found criminally negligent.

Following are some cases where administrators have been held personally responsible or had their licenses revoked because of breach of duty, violation of rules or codes, or certain criminal actions.

> In *Frye v. Kaladjian*, 617 NYS 2d 1003, Mary Anne Frye was the operator of a licensed group family day care facility. She was accused of violating State of New York regulations. An administrative law judge heard the case, found Frye guilty of the charges, and revoked her license as a day care provider.
>
> Frye then appealed to the supreme court of New York State, which held that the evidence showed that Frye failed to provide records to inspectors, that Frye allowed obstruction of exits at the facility, and that the facility was over capacity. The supreme court affirmed the decision of the administrative law judge and the revocation of the license.
>
> In *Sanchez v. Board of Examiners of Nursing Home Administrators*, 461 NYS 2d 920, there was an investigation by the special prosecutor for Medicaid fraud. Richard Sanchez, a nursing home administrator, was indicted on felony charges involving fraudulent use of the nursing facility business expense account for personal expenditures. Because of his

cooperation, he was permitted to withdraw his felony plea and plead to the misdemeanor of petty larceny. A sentence of three years' probation and $29,000 restitution to the state was imposed.

A charge of unethical conduct was also filed against Sanchez. The administrative law judge recommended that Sanchez be reprimanded but that his license not be revoked. However, the board of examiners suspended his license for 16 months, feeling that his crime was of a serious nature in the field of nursing home administration and noting that Sanchez had prior censure by the board for an unrelated matter.

Sanchez appealed the decision of the board of examiners to the New York State Supreme Court. The court held that a nursing home administrator convicted of a crime has committed unethical conduct and may be penalized in a variety of ways, including censure, licensure revocation, and licensure suspension, as the board in its discretion sees fit. The court upheld the suspension, saying that the 16-month suspension penalty was far less severe than what Sanchez could have gotten and not disproportionate to the offense committed.

In *Feuereisen v. Axelrod*, 473 NYS 2d 870, Aaron Feuereisen, a licensed administrator and a partner in the Far Rockaway Nursing Home, pled guilty to three misdemeanors—one count of conspiracy and two counts of willful violation of health laws. The guilty plea was a plea bargain whereby the original 29-count indictment against him for mismanagement of the nursing facility and its funds would be reduced to the three misdemeanor counts. Feuereisen was fined $2,500.

After his plea, the State Board of Examiners of Nursing Home Administrators found Feuereisen guilty of unethical conduct and suspended his license as a nursing home administrator for one year.

Feuereisen then appealed this decision to the supreme court of New York State, saying that the board had made a mistake in suspending his license on the basis of the criminal conviction. The court stated that, on previous occasions, they had held that a conviction of a crime was sufficient to satisfy the statutory standard of unethical conduct for purposes of disciplinary actions against nursing home administrators. The primary event triggering the discipline action is the conviction, not any admission of wrongdoing in the criminal proceeding. The court did not find the penalty of a one-year suspension of Feuereisen's license to be excessive. The malfeasance of the administrator was not so serious as to shock the consciousness of the court in revoking the suspension of the administrator's license for one year.

In the case of *Sreter v. Board of Examiners*, 460 NYS 2d 468, Susan Sreter, a licensed nursing home administrator, and her son, also a licensed administrator, served as coadministrators of the Nassau Nursing Home. In June 1977, after becoming aware of pending felony charges for fraudulent treatment of their personal expenses as nursing facility business deductions, they agreed to cooperate with the special investigator for nursing home corruption in return for negotiation of a plea agreement. The Sreters were allowed to plead guilty to a misdemeanor in full satisfaction of the more serious charges and sentenced to one year of probation.

After the sentence, the board of examiners charged them with unethical conduct, for which a range of penalties from censure to revocation of their nursing home administrator licenses could be imposed. The hearing officer recommended that the board censure the Sreters; the board suspended their licenses for 16 months.

The Sreters appealed the sentence to the Supreme Court, Appellate Division, New York State, which held that the proposed stipulation between the Department of Health and the Sreters limiting the penalty to censure did not affect in any way the deliberations of the board of examiners. The board of examiners said the crimes were serious, carrying a possible penalty of one year in prison and a $5,000 fine. The supreme court further held that the extent of the penalty was a matter for the full board to decide, even though the executive director of the board knew of the recommendation for censure by the hearing officer; in view of the offenses committed, the penalty was not disproportionate to the misconduct.

MEDICARE FRAUD AND ABUSE

Medicare fraud is costly to the health care system. The U.S. General Accounting Office estimates that provider fraud costs the public as much as 100 billion dollars yearly. The federal government has enacted numerous tools in its fight against crime and abuse in the Medicare and Medicaid programs.

Medicare and Medicaid Anti-Fraud and Abuse Statute

The administrator may be involved in civil or criminal acts under the Medicare and Medicaid Anti-Fraud and Abuse Statute. This criminal statute is applicable to all persons and to all services reimbursed by Medicare and Medicaid. In 1977, there was a great expansion of the Medicare and Medicaid Anti-Fraud and Abuse Amendments. Violations were made felonies, with a maximum of five years in prison and/or a $25,000 fine for each offense.

Section 1877 (Medicare) and Section 1909 (Medicaid) of the Social Security Act covered false statements and claims, kickbacks, bribes, and rebates; violations were considered misdemeanors. These sections are now under Section 1128(B) of the Social Security Act.

Stark Act

This civil statute applies to physicians and to specified services. The act resulted from a congressionally mandated study; in June 1988, Congress mandated that the Office of Inspector General (OIG) conduct a study on physician ownership of and compensation from the health care entities to which physicians make referrals. The study found that patients of referring physicians who owned or invested in independent clinical labs received 45 percent more laboratory services than all Medicare patients in general. Partly as a result of this study, in 1989 Congress enacted Section 1877 of the Social Security Act, which was the initial Stark Act.

Health Insurance Reportability and Accountability Act of 1996

This act expanded the Anti-Fraud and Abuse Statute by enhancing the government's ability to investigate and prosecute violations related to health care.

False Claims Act

This act expanded the Anti-Fraud and Abuse Statute. It emphasizes the making of false claims relating to all services. Under the act, it is a felony to make false statements or claims in connection with any services provided to Medicare or Medicaid patients. Such false statements are punishable by a fine of not more than $25,000 or imprisonment for not more than five years or both. False statements that are made by a person other than the one furnishing a service are misdemeanors.

It is a felony to make false statements or claims in connection with services provided to Medicare or Medicaid patients. False statements include:

- knowingly and willfully making a false statement or representation of a material fact in seeking to obtain any benefit or payment
- fraudently concealing or failing to disclose information affecting the right to a payment
- converting any benefit or payment rightfully belonging to another
- presenting a claim for a physician's service, knowing that the individual who furnished the service was not licensed as a physician

The false claims provision of the Anti-Fraud and Abuse Statute has been used to prosecute providers who falsify billing records or who attempt to get paid for services not provided.

Kickbacks

Under the Anti-Fraud and Abuse Statute, the offering, giving, receiving, or solicitation of payments in exchange for the referral of Medicare or Medicaid business is a felony. Conviction carries a fine of up to $25,000 or imprisonment for not more than five years or both.

However, the statute provides exceptions for certain arrangements and practices that are not considered violations if they meet criteria. Exceptions include space and equipment rental arrangements, personnel service and certain management contracts, referral services, discount arrangements, payments to bona fide employees, and group purchasing organizations. Other safe harbors specify payment practices that are not considered remuneration and, therefore, are exempt from the anti-kickback laws.

Civil Monetary Penalties

There are provisions for civil penalties for engaging in fraudulent activities against the Medicare and Medicaid program. The Civil Monetary Penalties Law (CMPL) was enacted in 1981 and, at that time, provided a penalty of up to $2,000 for each violation. The final regulations were published on January 29, 1992. Conduct in violation carrying civil penalties includes:

- A person knowing of a service that was not provided as claimed.
- A physician's service rendered by a person not licensed as a physician or who obtained his or her license through misrepresentation.
- A service furnished during a period in which the person was excluded from participation or had his or her provider agreement terminated.
- A pattern of medically unnecessary services or supplies.

Generally speaking, the CMP offenses are now punishable at $10,000 for each item violated and an assessment up to three times the amount claimed for each item or service violated.

Civil Monetary Penalty Procedures

The secretary of Health and Human Services may start an action for a civil monetary penalty up to six years after a claim is first presented. A person is entitled to notice and a formal administrative hearing on the record before a penalty or assessment is determined. The secretary is required to take into account aggravating or mitigating circumstances when determining the scope of any penalty or assessment. The OIG may settle without consent of the administrative law judge.

An entity may appeal the initial decision of the administrative law judge to the Departmental Appeals Board by filing a notice of appeal with the board within 30 days of the date of the initial decision. There is also a provision for appeal to the U.S. Court of Appeals.

Home Health Care Fraud

In today's society, Americans are living longer than ever before. An increasing number of elderly receive in-home care and are dependent upon family and health care providers to attend to their health care needs. Home care services may be provided by nurses, home nursing aides, speech therapists, and physical therapists, all under a physician-certified plan of care. Home health care is a new breeding ground for fraud.

The Department of Health and Human Services has a program, Operation Restore Trust, that is an anti-fraud enforcement act aimed at nursing facilities, home health care agencies, and durable equipment suppliers. This alert was issued by the OIG to target claims for services not provided, claims for visits not authorized by a physician, claims for visits not made, and claims for beneficiaries not homebound.

CHAPTER 9

Labor Law and Labor Relations

Labor relations and labor law are important in the operation of a long-term health care facility. There are two basic areas of labor law to consider: federal and state. Federal labor law is applied only when a federal court has jurisdiction under the United States Constitution. Interstate Commerce Commission (ICC) activity expands the role of the federal government in labor relations. State labor laws apply to those business activities that are intrastate (within the state). Labor laws relating to workers' compensation, child and female labor, and right to work are customarily handled by the state. If a state statute recognizes employees' rights to organize, bargain collectively, and strike, broad language usually extends these rights to state and municipal employees.

BASIC LABOR LAWS

In the early 1930s, during the country's severest depression, political pressure in Congress increased to address general dissatisfaction with judicial restrictions in labor relations. Federal labor laws were passed to protect civil rights and discrimination in three basic areas, as discussed below.

Protection of the Employee's Rights To Organize, Encouragement of Collective Bargaining, and Elimination of Unfair Labor Practices

Norris–La Guardia Act

In 1932, Congress passed the Norris–La Guardia Act (also called the Federal Anti-Injunction Act). This act allowed employees full freedom of association, self-organization, and designation of representatives of their own choosing; negotiation of terms and conditions of employment; and freedom from employer interference, restraint, and coercion. Further, it recognized employees' right to freedom from employer interference (for example, wrongful use of injunctions) in their efforts at self-organization and other activities for the purpose of collective bargaining.

National Labor Relations Act (Wagner Act)

In 1935, Senator Robert Wagner, then chairman of the National Labor Board, led the fight for this act, also known as the NLRA. It guaranteed the right of employees to join a labor organization and bargain collectively through representatives of their own choosing. The act also detailed specific unfair employer labor practices and created the National Labor Relations Board (NLRB) to enforce its provisions by determining appropriate bargaining units, supervising elections at the request of workers, certifying duly chosen unions, taking testimony about unfair employer practices, and issuing cease and desist orders. In 1937, the U.S. Supreme Court, following the case of *NLRB v. Jones and Laughlin Steel Co.*, 301 US 1, declared the Wagner Act constitutional.

Taft-Hartley Act

Because of the tremendous growth and power of unions for the next 10 years, Congress, in 1947, amended the National Labor Relations Act by enacting the Taft-Hartley or Labor Management Relations Act. This act reorganized the NLRB and included unfair union labor practices covering such topics as closed shop, damages resulting from broken union contracts and/or strikes, 60-day cooling-off period before strikes, publishing financial statements and political contributions, bargaining requirements, boycotts by unions not involved in a dispute, and strikes over work assignments.

Landrum-Griffin Act

The Landrum-Griffin Act of 1959 was a result of a congressional investigation of unions. This law provided for the following:

- union member rights
  - equal rights with all other members in voting and participating in union activities

- freedom of union members to express their opinion
- a voice in proposed increases in dues
- protection against being fired or expelled from the union without a written list of charges
- freedom to sue, testify, and communicate with any legislator without being limited by the union
- elections
  - Elections must be by secret ballot.
  - Members must have reasonable opportunity to nominate candidates.
  - Members must have sufficient notice of elections.
  - Voting for each candidate must be reported local by local.
  - Elections must be carried out according to the constitution and bylaws of the unions.
- union reporting
  - required by law to file copies of their constitution and bylaws with the secretary of labor and to file annual reports on conduct of their internal affairs
  - must report, in their annual fiscal statement, compensation to officers and employees of the union making in excess of $10,000
- trusteeships
  - Control of a subordinate union by a parent organization can be established and administered only to correct corruption, ensure unions' duties as bargaining representatives are fulfilled, and ensure that union contracts are fulfilled.
  - A parent union is prevented from usurping power and funds from a subordinate union.

Protection Regarding Hours, Wages, and Child Labor

Walsh-Healy Act

The Walsh-Healy Act of 1936 applies to workers employed by firms that have government contracts in excess of $10,000. Penalties for infractions of the act can be fines up to $10,000 and six months in jail. Its two basic provisions are:

1. All work in excess of eight hours each day must be paid at time and a half.

2. Minimum wages based upon the prevailing rates in the community must be paid.

Fair Labor Standards Act of 1938

This act has been amended many times. The amendments are highly technical and complicated. The 1968 amendment prescribes minimum wages and maximum hours (40-hour workweek) of employment, requires payment of time and a half for overtime, sets a minimum age of 16 years for general employment, and requires employers to maintain records of hours worked and wages paid. Penalties for infraction of the provisions can be fines up to $10,000 and six months in jail. This act covers all firms or persons engaged in interstate or foreign commerce. It exempts executives, administrative personnel and professionals, farm laborers, and domestic servants.

A section specifically addresses employment in hospitals and establishments caring for the sick, aged, or mentally ill. It generally provides that a work period of 14 consecutive days is accepted for purposes of computing overtime, if the employee and employer have agreed to this and the employee receives overtime for more than 80 hours in any 14-day workweek.

There is also an amendment adding a training wage (85 percent of the minimum wage) for new workers in nonagricultural jobs with less than 60 days of cumulative work experience.

Equal Pay Act of 1963

This act is an amendment to the Fair Labor Standards Act. It prohibits employers from discriminating on the basis of sex in the payment of wages for equal work. Pay differentials may exist, but they must be justified on the basis of skill, efforts, responsibility, working conditions, seniority, merit, or some factor other than sex.

Employment Discrimination

Equal Employment Opportunity Act of 1972

This act amended Title VII of the Civil Rights Act of 1964 and prohibits any form of employment discrimination by companies, labor unions, and employment agencies on the basis of race, color, religion, sex, or national origin. The Equal Employment Opportunity Commission was created to provide an enforcement procedure including investigations, attempts at conciliation, and suits filed on behalf of the complainant.

Vocational Rehabilitation Act of 1973 (Section 503)

This act requires holders of federal government contracts in excess of $2,500 to take affirmative action to employ and advance in employment qualified physically and mentally handicapped individuals.

Age Discrimination in Employment Act of 1967, as Amended in 1978

This act prohibits employment discrimination against those between the ages of 40 and 70, forbids forced retirement based on age before age 70, permits compulsory retirement for executives who are entitled to pensions of $27,000 per year or more, and authorizes jury trials in certain cases.

NATIONAL LABOR RELATIONS BOARD

The NLRB carries out the policies of the National Labor Relations Act and includes a five-member board and its staff; the general counsel and its staff; and 50 regional and field offices located in major cities. The board has two major functions.

1. To supervise and conduct representation elections.
2. To adjudicate employer and union unfair labor practices.

NLRB activities are set in motion only when requested in writing and filed with the proper NLRB office. Such requests are called *petitions* in the case of elections and *charges* in the case of unfair labor practices.

Procedure of NLRB Regarding Unfair Labor Practice

A charge is filed with the NLRB Regional Director by an employee, employer, labor union, or individual alleging an unfair labor practice. The party charged is called the *respondent* and is notified that an investigation of the alleged violation will be conducted. If no settlement is reached, an unfair labor practice hearing is conducted before an administrative law judge, who makes findings and recommendations to the board based on the record of the hearing. All parties are authorized to appeal the administrative law judge's decision directly to the board. The board considers the information provided and the data collected. If it believes an unfair labor practice has occurred, an order to cease and desist such practices and to take appropriate affirmative action is issued. A cease-and-desist order directs the violators to stop whatever activities were deemed unfair labor practices. The board exercises discretion in determining appropriate affirmative action by issuing such orders to:

- **employers**, who may direct them to:
  - Disestablish an employer-dominated company union.
  - Offer employees immediate and full reinstatement to their former positions and pay them back their wages and interest.
  - Upon request, bargain collectively with the exclusive bargaining representative of the employees.
- **unions**, which may direct them to:
  - Refund excessive or illegally collected dues plus interest.
  - Upon request, bargain collectively in good faith with the prescribed employer.

Federal Courts and NLRB Proceedings

The district court, under the enforcement provision of the act, serves two major purposes:

1. To provide injunctive relief by issuing a temporary restraining order (TRO) where appropriate.
2. To review appealed decisions and orders of the NLRB.

The court of appeals may enforce an order upon reviewing the orders of the district court, return it for reconsideration, alter it, or set it aside. The final appeal is to the U.S. Supreme Court.

The NLRB's Jurisdictional Standards Relating to the Health Care Industry as of 1974

These standards apply to privately operated health care institutions: hospitals (at least $250,000 total annual volume of business), nursing facilities, visiting nurse associations, related facilities (at least $100,000 total annual volume of business), and all other types of private health care institutions (at least $250,000 total annual volume of business). The statutory definition includes "any hospital, convalescent hospital, HMO, health clinic, nursing home, skilled nursing facility, or other institution devoted to the care of the sick."

UNION ORGANIZATION

One of the prime considerations of the nursing home administrator regarding labor relations and the nursing facility is the reasons why employees in a facility would want to organize. Generally speaking, employees unionize due to poor supervision, job dissatisfaction, or a lack of good employee benefits and personnel policies that are clearly written and distributed to all employees. Poor policies in this area, improperly communicated, can lead to problems of inconsistent treatment of personnel, misunderstandings, unrest, rumors, jealousy, and high turnover. Personnel policies should include an explanation of the facility's standard wage program, vacations, paid holidays, sick leave and hospitalization benefits, funeral leave, grievance procedure, promotion policies, and discipline procedures at a minimum; these should be reviewed and updated periodically so that they remain competitive. Administrators need to be familiar with personnel policies and benefits being paid in their own areas and throughout the state.

Internal communication is of prime importance as well. If there is a lack of communication, employees may not feel part of the team, be insecure in their jobs, or feel that there is no outlet for grievances. Suggestions for improving communications include: ·

- regular monthly department head meetings with the administrator
- regular department head meetings with employees

- publication of an internal house organ or newspaper
- use of suggestion programs for input by employees
- recognition programs, whereby outstanding employees are identified and given public recognition

Campaign Initiation and Preelection Campaigns

Union organizing campaigns usually start at the grassroots level of employees. Either the workers themselves ask the union to help or union organizers identify a facility with problems and get in touch with the workers by handbill or personal contact. A union representative may approach department heads or other administrative personnel in person or by letter or telephone to discuss union organizing or try to deliver union authorization cards or petitions; he or she may distribute union literature at the entrance to the employees' parking area. Such actions or materials should be referred to the human resources department or facility administrator immediately. Issues regarding employment in the facility should not be discussed with the union representative. Authorization cards or petitions that have been dropped off at a work station should be placed into an envelope, sealed, and referred to the aforementioned persons; a management employee should witness the placement of these materials into the envelope.

The vital first step is to establish a two-way communication between the facility employees and the union. Next comes the educational process, during which the union points out employees' problems, compares wages at their facility to wages at unionized facilities, and explains the role of the union in helping to satisfy job-related needs. Exhibit 9–1 lists employee concerns and union answers to those questions.

The union makes every attempt to convince the workers to complete union authorization cards and to support the forthcoming organizing campaign by wearing union buttons, attending meetings, and signing up others. Some of the most effective ways to do this are one-to-one contact, peer contact, persuasion, and high-quality, professionally designed written communications. The NLRB recognizes that both union and management have the right to conduct "free and vigorous" campaigns and that exaggerations, half-truths, inaccuracies, and name calling, although not condoned, are not grounds for setting aside an election. However, speeches and other actions must be within the NLRB guidelines. The occurrence of an unfair labor practice during a critical phase of the preelection campaign can result

Exhibit 9–1 Union Solutions to Employee Problems

Employee Concern	Union Answer
Desire for improvement of present fringe benefits	Negotiate better benefits for bargaining unit employees.
Earns less than deserved compared to others doing similar work	Emphasize comparable wages (local, regional, national); provide data from other unions and Department of Labor and wage surveys.
Desire for additional fringe benefits	Negotiate new benefits, such as dental insurance or legal aid.
Difficulty getting work days and hours changed	Negotiate work schedule procedures with rules and policies that are administered fairly and in accordance with the contract.
Inadequate time for leisure activities	Attempt to obtain shorter hours and workweek, more holidays, and longer vacations for time worked.
Skills underutilized in present job	Negotiate promotion policies and procedures.
Unpleasant work environment	Negotiate working conditions and transfer opportunities; institute safety and health committees.

in the overturn of an election. Some of the doctrines or standards are as follows:

- **Totality of conduct doctrine**—In determining whether or not a specific statement or incident violates NLRB guidelines, the isolated incidents (campaign speeches, etc.) must be considered as a whole within the scope of the general circumstances of the campaign. While one act or speech may violate guidelines, it cannot characterize the entire campaign but *can* indicate that other specific violations may have occurred to justify further investigation.

- **Employer or union speeches**—Speeches that are substantial departures from the truth can constitute interference with the employees' right to a fair election. Preelection campaign speeches must not:
  - Misrepresent material facts or contain similar trickery.
  - Present information by a person known to employees to have special knowledge about that information.
  - Present information so close to the election that the other party has no opportunity for an effective reply.
  - Make any misrepresentation that may reasonably have a significant effect upon the election.
  - Lack qualification to evaluate the statements made.

- **Captive audience and the 24-hour rule**—Neither the facility nor the union may make a captive audience speech monopolizing the employees within 24 hours of the election. The facility may deny a union's request to use its premises during working hours to reply to a facility's speech as long as the union has another means to effectively communicate with the employees. However, if the facility has created a serious campaign imbalance and the union has no acceptable means of communicating with employees, the NLRB and courts may grant the union access to facility bulletin boards, parking lots, and entrances to accomplish this communication.

- **Polling employees**—Polling of employees by the facility is not considered an unlawful interference if the following safeguards are employed:
  - The purpose of the inquiry is to determine the accuracy of a union claim that it represents the majority of the employees, and this purpose is clearly communicated to the employees.
  - The poll is conducted by secret ballot and assurances are given against employer reprisal.
  - The facility has not committed any unfair labor practices.

- **Distribution of union literature on facility property**—The NLRB and courts have long held that employees may not be prohibited from distributing union organizational materials in nonworking areas on their own time unless the facility can show that such activity would disrupt its operations, employee work, or discipline. For example, employees of nursing facilities may not distribute such literature in areas designated for residents but may do so in the cafeteria. The facility cannot prohibit distribution of union materials on the basis that they discuss (in part) such political issues as right-to-work laws and minimum wage.

Administration's Actions during a Union Organizational Drive

Administrators often learn of union organizing attempts from department heads or from rank and file employees and through actual observation before they receive the official notification (by letter or telegram) from the union demanding recognition. Early signs of concerted activity among employees include:

- Complaints are made by groups instead of individuals. The nature and frequency of the complaints change. Grapevine rumors increase regarding employee dissatisfaction.
- Employees avoid supervisors and are not willing to share information, sometimes baiting them in an effort to make them lose their temper.
- Usually good workers perform poorly while poor workers perform well.
- Employees working in different departments and at different job levels get together to discuss related job problems.
- Strangers appear at employee gathering places.
- Union literature circulates.

Some facilities react violently; others do little to acknowledge any union attempt to organize the employees. Administrators may tell their employees about their opposition and urge them not to sign union authorization cards. Generally, the employer should not intimidate or retaliate against employees who are interested in working with a union. Employers should *not*:

- Ask employees to express their thoughts about a union or its officers.
- Prevent employees from soliciting union members on their free time on company premises, as long as the literature does not interfere with the work being performed by others.

- Threaten that union activity may result in loss of jobs or job status, reduction of income, or discontinuation of privileges or benefits presently enjoyed by the employees.
- Use intimidating language designed to influence employees in the exercise of their right to belong or refrain from belonging to a union.
- Actually discharge, discipline, or lay off employees because of their activities on behalf of the union.
- Ask employees whether or not they intend to sign a card or vote in an election.
- Discriminate against employees actively supporting the union by intentionally assigning them undesirable work.
- Exhibit conduct that indicates to employees that they are being watched for participation in union activities.
- Promise employees an increase in pay, a promotion, or special favors or benefits if they stay out of the union or vote against it.
- Suggest to employees that they will be penalized if they vote for the union.
- Urge employees to try to persuade others to oppose the union or to stay out of it.
- Tell employees that the facility will refuse to bargain meaningfully with a union if the union is elected to represent them. The facility may not make false statements about the union or the organizational campaign.
- Refuse to bargain with union on union membership or compulsory union membership.
- Prevent distribution of union materials in nonworking areas (locker rooms, employee cafeteria, parking lots) or ban union buttons or decals on employee personal property (uniforms, lunchboxes).

Generally, employers have the right to deal honestly with staff, give correct information, and express their opinions as to why the facility does not want to deal with a union. It is recommended that employers:

- Inform employees that there may be disadvantages of belonging to a union, outlining such things as loss of income because of strikes, requirements to serve on a picket line, the expense of paying dues, and the expense of fines and assessment.

- Tell employees that the nursing facility prefers to deal directly with them rather than through an intermediary or the union organization, which may not understand the facility's problems and difficulties. Let them know that the administrative staff, including supervisors, are willing to discuss any complaints with them.
- Point out to employees the pay and fringe benefits that they now enjoy and that jobs and benefits are protected only as long as the facility operates efficiently so that revenues exceed expenses.
- Let employees know that they are free to join or not to join the union, and that if they do join, the facility will not be prejudiced against them. Anyone may campaign against unionization if that is his or her position.
- Express opinions regarding unions and union leaders, even though those opinions may be uncomplimentary. However, it should be clear that these are *personal* opinions.
- Inform employees of misleading or untrue statements made by union organizers.
- Tell employees that, if the union belongs to an international union, the probability is that the international union will try to dominate the local union.
- Lay off, discipline, or discharge employees for cause as long as such action is the customary practice and there is no discrimination between union and nonunion members.
- Tell employees that no union can make a company agree to anything it does not wish to or pay any more than it is willing or able to pay, and that all clauses in a collective bargaining agreement must, in fact, be agreed upon by both parties.
- Let employees know how their wages, benefits, and working conditions compare with those of other nursing facilities in the area as long as information is factual. Remind them of regularly scheduled increases in wages and fringe benefits.
- Relate to employees any experiences the employer may have had with unions.
- Tell employees that if the majority decides to join a union, work problems will have to be discussed through the union and no longer individually with the facility.

- Point out that government regulations, third-party payers, or industrial economic limitations may prevent the facility from meeting union promises.
- Prevent, in an impartial manner, distribution of union literature during working hours in work areas of the facility, the placing of union decals or banners on facility equipment or walls, and the wearing of union buttons by employees with extensive resident contact.

Representation Election Procedure

Filing a Petition for Election

The unionization procedure is started when the potential bargaining representative for the employees files a petition with the NLRB for an election where the employees in a bargaining unit will vote for or against union representation. The NLRB is authorized to conduct an election only when such a petition is filed by an employee, group of employees, any individual or labor organization, or an employer. If filed by an employee or on behalf of employees, the petition must be supported by evidence (usually by authorization cards) that a substantial interest in union representation exists (30 percent of the bargaining unit). Further, it must show that the employer has denied a request by the union to recognize it as an employee representative.

After receiving a petition, the NLRB promptly notifies the facility and requests a list of employees; a facility is not required to submit a list of employees but usually complies as an act of good faith. Next, the NLRB arranges a conference with the facility and union to discuss the possibility of a "consent election." If both sides agree to the appropriate bargaining unit, voter eligibility, ballot, and time and place for the election, a consent election is held. If either party refuses to agree on any of these items, a formal hearing to settle these matters is requested and conducted.

Name and Address Rule

Within seven days after the regional director of the NLRB approves a consent election or directs an election, the NLRB may require the employer to provide a list of names and addresses of all eligible voters in the bargaining unit to the director. This information is made available to the union. Refusal to comply can be interpreted as bad faith on the part of the employer and cause the election to be set aside or the NLRB to seek the names and addresses by subpoena.

Election Investigation and Hearing

If the union and management officials do not agree to a consent election, the NLRB must investigate the petition, hold a hearing, if necessary, and then direct an election if it finds there is a question of employee representation. The following are questions to be answered by the investigation:

- Does the NLRB have jurisdiction?
- What is an appropriate bargaining unit?
- Does substantial interest in representation (30 percent) exist among employees in the unit?
- Are there any barriers to an election in the form of existing unions, prior elections, or present labor agreements?

Appropriate Bargaining Unit

The bargaining unit is a grouping of jobs or positions in which two or more employees share common employment interests and conditions and that is eligible for union representation and to bargain collectively. Determination of the appropriate bargaining unit is left to the discretion of the NLRB. The NLRB's determination of a bargaining unit strongly influences whether or not the union will win the election. Therefore, the composition of a bargaining unit is of vital importance to nursing facility administrators. A bargaining unit may include registered nurses (RNs), professional employees, technical employees (LPNs), service/maintenance employees (housekeeping, dietary), office/clerical, etc. In 1991, the U.S. Supreme Court upheld the NLRB in allowing health care facilities to have up to eight separate bargaining units (*American Hospital Association vs. NLRB*, 899 F2d 651).

The NLRB's discretion has been somewhat limited because professional employees cannot be included in a unit composed of both professional and nonprofessional employees unless a majority of the professional employees vote to be included in a mixed unit, and because agricultural laborers, public employees, independent contractors, supervisors, and managers are excluded from bargaining units.

It should be noted that under the NLRA, the term *supervisor* means any individual having authority in the interest of the employer to hire, transfer, suspend, lay off, recall, promote, discharge, assign, reward, or discipline other employees, or having responsibility to direct such employees to adjust their grievances, or effectively to recommend such action—if, in connection with their jobs, the exercise of such authority is not of a merely routine or clerical nature, but requires the use of independent judgment. The importance of supervisory status is that supervisors are not employees within the meaning of the NLRA and have no right to vote in elections for determination of bargaining representatives. As expected, there are times when it is not clear whether an employee is a professional, a supervisor, or perhaps not either.

In the case of *University Nursing Home et al.*, 168 NLRB 53, the employer sought to exclude an LPN from a bargaining unit composed of housekeeping, kitchen, and maintenance employees on the basis that she was a professional employee. The NLRB never specifically determined the LPN's status as a professional person but instead found that she was a supervisor and as such was to be excluded from the housekeeping bargaining unit. The NLRB noted that the LPN was in charge of one of the three wings of the facility, supervised the work of three nurses' aides and one orderly, carried out orders and treatments prescribed by residents' doctors, reviewed residents' charts to make certain that proper medications and diet were given, and observed and reported symptoms to the head RN.

Eligibility of Voters

Usually, those employees on the payroll just before the date of the election are eligible. Exceptions are made to allow employees who are on sick leave, vacation, or temporary leave or who are laid off to vote in the election.

The Representation Election

The election to determine whether or not the majority of the employees in an appropriate bargaining unit want to be represented for collective bargaining purposes is conducted by NLRB officials within 45 days of the petition filing. Usually, the voting draws up to 90 percent of the eligible voters. Using a ballot with the appropriate company and union designations, a secret ballot election is usually conducted under NLRB supervision during working hours at the employer's location. Majority rules; the NLRA defines *majority* as a simple majority rule—50 percent plus one of those voting. If the majority votes against the union, no representation election can be held for 12 months. If a union receives the majority of the votes, the NLRA certifies it as the exclusive bargaining agent of the employees in the bargaining unit. After the votes are counted, both parties have five days to file objections alleging misconduct or to challenge the ballots of voters it believes should not have voted in the election.

LABOR AGREEMENTS AND COLLECTIVE BARGAINING

If a union is successful in obtaining representation, the next step in the labor negotiations process is the collective bargaining agreement. The NLRA imposes mutual obligations on the facility and the union to bargain collectively.

Collective Bargaining Agreement

A bargaining team consisting of nursing facility and union representatives is established and an initial meeting scheduled to establish procedures and proposals to be included in the labor agreement. Available collective bargaining agreements relating to similar health care facilities in its area are reviewed. All activities that take place are recorded. The facility usually negotiates nonmonetary items such as recognition, management rights, grievance procedures, union rights, seniority rights, arbitration agencies, and subject matter first and then considers monetary items such as wages, vacations, paid holidays, and sick leave. Other subjects negotiated include compensation of employees on union committees during negotiation periods (that is, not a facility responsibility), composition of the bargaining team (members of the employee committee representing the union not on the facility bargaining team), time and frequency of future meetings, and settlement of disputes. State statutes usually provide that voluntary negotitation is the preferred method of resolving labor disputes between nursing facilities and their employees.

Administering the Agreement

Once the labor agreement is negotiated, great care must be given to its execution; facility rights established at the bargaining table may be lost if the contract is haphazardly administered.

Unions generally administer labor agreements within the facility through shop stewards. Stewards are employees who are either appointed by the union or elected by fellow employees to supervise the labor agreement on behalf of the union. Employees turn to their departmental steward or to the facility's chief steward for advice about whether or not to file a grievance to protest an alleged contract violation. If a worker is called by a department head for an interview that the employee believes may result in disciplinary action, the employee has the right to insist upon the presence of the union stewards.

Top administration must ensure that its own representatives understand the significant aspects of the agreement. Department heads who are unaware of the essential aspects of the agreement may unintentionally violate unions' rights and the contract may thus be eroded. One of the best ways to communicate the terms of a newly negotiated labor agreement to the key personnel in the facility is through an extensive inservice training program. The problem of discipline is of singular concern. Quite often, department heads believe that workers may not be discharged under a collective bargaining agreement. To deal with this misconception and to ensure that discipline is administered for appropriate reasons, department heads need to be trained in the use of progressive discipline, where an oral warning is followed by a written warning, and so on.

Notice Requirements

The NLRA specifies notice requirements that must be satisfied before a contract can be modified or terminated.

- The act requires that the party seeking the change give at least 60 days' written notice prior to the time that the agreement expires or, if there is no expiration date, 60 days prior to the time the party desires to make such termination or modification.
- If no agreement is reached within 30 days, the party wishing to terminate or modify the agreement must notify the Federal Mediation

and Conciliation Service (FMCS) that a labor dispute exists. The FMCS helps mediate the dispute if called by one of the parties to do so.

Subject Matter of Negotiations

The NLRA requires parties to bargain over the subjects within the three broad categories of:

1. **wages**—shift differentials, severance pay, rents for facility-owned housing
2. **hours**—number, length, and hours of a shift and length of a workday
3. **other terms and conditions**—price of food in facility cafeteria, workloads, union access to the premises, management rights, promotions, and compulsory retirement

Subjects falling within these categories are called the *mandatory* or *statutory* subjects of bargaining; it is illegal for either party to refuse to negotiate them.

Subjects that fall outside mandatory categories are known as *permissive* or *discretionary*. The parties may but are not legally bound to bargain these subjects. It is illegal to precondition agreement negotiations upon a permissive subject or to bring negotiation to an impasse because of insistence upon a permissive subject. Further, it is illegal for a union to strike or for management to lock out employees because of a disagreement over a permissive subject.

Duties of the Exclusive Bargaining Agent and Employer

The bargaining representative chosen by the majority of the employees in the appropriate unit has the duty to represent equally and fairly all employees in that unit. The employer has a comparable obligation to bargain in good faith with the exclusive bargaining agent and to refuse to bargain with another union seeking to represent the employees.

What Is Bargaining in Good Faith?

The most subtle and complicated requirement of the NLRB is that parties negotiate in good faith. The NLRA defines the obligation to bargain in good faith as "The performance of the mutual obligation of the employer and the representative of the employees to meet at reasonable times and confer in good faith with respect to wages, hours, and other terms and conditions of employment." Both the NLRB and the courts have said that a good-faith attitude is one that expresses an open mind and a sincere desire to reach agreement. Although one ingredient of good-faith bargaining is willingness by each party to discuss the other's proposals, mere discussion is not enough. Surface or shadow bargaining is where one party engages in extensive discussion but never reaches agreement on anything. Tactics designed solely to delay negotiations may violate the NLRA.

Failure to reach agreement or to make a concession is not in itself bad-faith bargaining. However, unwillingness to reach common ground on any significant issue might be viewed "in totality of the circumstances" or in combination with other factors—that is, as evidence that the party lacks good faith.

The facility is not helpless in collective bargaining when the parties reach an impasse. It is entitled to lock out employees in order to compel a union to accede to management's position where mandatory subjects are involved in the negotiations. From a practical viewpoint, a facility rarely locks out its employees.

Duty To Furnish Information to a Union

The duty to furnish necessary information to a collective bargaining representative is made clear by case law and the NLRB. The fundamental general principle is that a facility must furnish a union, upon request, sufficient information to enable it to bargain intelligently and to police the administration of an existing agreement. However, the duty to supply information is not absolute. A facility is not required to supply information on wages, hours, or other conditions of employment merely because of union request; the union must show that the requested information is relevant to the bargaining process or to the administration of the agreement.

Compliance with a request for relevant information by a union must be made promptly. Whether a delay in the furnishing of requested information is so unreasonable as to constitute unlawful refusal depends upon the individual fact situation. In one case, the NLRB held that a two-month unexplained delay in providing relevant information was unlawful.

Unilateral Changes

The duty to bargain is a continuous obligation. If the facility seeks to make a substantive change in the agreement, such change must be negotiated with the union before it is implemented. An impasse is the inability of the parties to agree upon one or more issues. When an impasse is reached, the duty to bargain is suspended. The facility is then free to make unilateral changes consistent with its offers to the union. The union may waive its right to bargain about certain issues.

Decertification Procedures

Whenever employees believe that the union is not representing the interest of the majority, a decertification procedure is available. Any employee, group of employees, or employee representative may file a petition for a decertification election 12 months after the union is certified or upon expiration of the labor agreement, not to exceed three years. The facility cannot petition for a decertification election; however, it can question the union's majority status and petition the NLRB for a representation election. There is a 30 percent requirement for decertification; 30 percent of the employees must support the petition.

STRIKES, PICKETING, AND SECONDARY ACTIVITY

A strike is a planned stoppage of work by employees that slows down or interrupts operations. Some state statutes are clear in allowing strikes to occur. Before the passage of the NLRA in 1935, strikes and other job-related acts were governed solely by state laws (with the exception of the federal anti-injunction laws). While most state laws did not expressly prohibit strikes by employees, neither did they expressly permit them and, frequently, a facility could persuade the state courts to enjoin a strike. The NLRA now protects the right of employees to engage in "concerted activities," including the right to "a concerted stoppage of work by employees" or strike.

The three types of strikes in which employees may engage are primary economic, unfair labor practice, and recognitional. The NLRA requires labor organizations to give written notice to health care institutions and the

FMCS at least 10 days before engaging in any strike, picketing, or other concerted refusal to work. If a union fails to give this notice, it is guilty of an unfair labor practice.

Economic and Unfair Labor Practice Strikes

The two major kinds of lawful strikes are economic and unfair labor practice. Under the NLRA, strikers retain their employee status while on strike. However, a striker's rights to reinstatement to a job may depend on whether the strike is economic or unfair labor practice.

An **economic strike** usually concerns wages, hours, or working conditions. When employees engage in a lawful primary economic strike against a facility, they may not be disciplined or discharged because they do so. The facility may replace them, either temporarily or permanently, because it must continue to operate. Economic strikers are generally disenfranchised for 12 months after a strike begins. Economic strikers who are temporarily replaced are generally entitled to reinstatement at such time as they make an unconditional offer to return to work. Economic strikers who are permanently replaced are not entitled to automatic reinstatement when the strike is over. They do not lose status as employees; however, they must be placed on a preferential hiring list and offered reinstatement when future vacancies arise, unless they refuse an unconditional offer of reinstatement after a strike is over, abandon the job, or are discharged for serious strike misconduct.

An **unfair labor strike** is one that protests a facility's labor practices. Unlike economic strikers, unfair labor practice strikers have a legal right to reinstatement and may not be permanently replaced. The facility must reinstate them upon their unconditional application for reinstatement, even if their jobs have been filled. An unfair labor practice striker is entitled to vote in any election held at any time.

Illegal Strikes

Certain strikes are unlawful because their purpose is illegal or because the tactics used during the strike are illegal and are not protected under the NLRA. Employees who participate in an illegal strike are not protected by the NLRA; they lose their employee status. They may be discharged with no right to reinstatement and are ineligible to vote in any representation election. Examples of strikes that are illegal or unprotected under the NLRA are:

- sit-down strikes, where strikers remain on the facility premises and refuse to leave after being instructed to do so
- strikes not complying with notice periods outlined in the NLRA
- partial or intermittent strikes or slowdowns
- strikes with illegal aims
- work assignment strikes
- strikes in violation of a no-strike clause in a collective bargaining agreement

Picketing

Picketing is the act of patrolling by one or more persons of a place related to a labor dispute. Picketing may be conducted by employees or nonemployees. Like strikes, some picketing is subject to regulations.

The 1974 amendments to the NLRA added requirements with respect to strikes and picketing in an attempt to reduce the interruption of health care services. A board of inquiry was created and is called in if a dispute threatens to interrupt health care in a particular community.

Remedies for Illegal Strikes and Picketing

Peaceful strikes and picketing are subject to regulation exclusively by the NLRB and the NLRA. Violent strikes and picketing are subject to regulation both by the NLRA and by the state courts. Violent strikes are primarily a police matter that is left to the states. Only peaceful strike and picketing activity is federally preempted. A facility confronted with a violent labor dispute has a number of options.

- Seek an injunction and damages from a state court.
- File an unfair labor practice charge under the NLRA.
- Ask the NLRB to seek an injunction from a federal court.
- File a criminal complaint if criminal statutes are violated.

Although it is difficult for a facility to secure injunctive relief in the federal courts, such relief is available if a union violates a no-strike clause of a collective bargaining agreement that contains mandatory grievance and arbitration procedures. An injunction is an order issued by a court directing that a certain act be done or not done. Persons failing to comply with court orders are in contempt of court and may be subjected to fines or imprisonment.

LEGAL PROTECTION FOR THE NURSING FACILITY

Nursing facilities must provide safe health care to their residents and must also respect the rights of unionized staff members who provide that care. Unionized staff members may include aides, orderlies, housekeepers, and maintenance personnel. Strikes and resident abuse are two areas involving bargaining units that can seriously jeopardize resident care and facility reputation. When it interferes with residents' routines, administration of medication, and medical emergencies, a strike significantly undermines routine services and stability. The facility could be held liable for the consequences of job actions of nonprofessionals.

Protection against Union Strikes

Protection against work slowdowns or stoppages can be achieved through the contract provisions of the collective bargaining agreement, which require that all disputes (contract enforcement, bad-faith bargaining) and all grievances (dismissal for resident abuse) be submitted to a grievance committee and then for binding arbitration. The agreement must be comprehensive enough to require that all disputes and all grievances between the facility and members of the bargaining unit be resolved through binding arbitration and that employees be prohibited from engaging in a strike or job action. A no-strike clause prevents cessation of work unless the facility refuses to comply with specific procedures relating to dispute or grievance resolution. The union may be found guilty of breach of contract and subject to injunction, damages, and other relief outlined in the collective bargaining agreement if direct or inferred union support of a strike is determined.

Protection against Resident Abuse

The nursing facility needs to determine definite procedures regarding employees suspected of resident abuse before health- and life-threatening consequences occur. There should be a statement of the facility's disciplinary procedures in the collective bargaining agreement, personnel manuals, and employee job descriptions and contracts. Acceptable behavior must be established that is binding on day-to-day providers. Although the termination of an employee may rid the facility of a real threat, facility disciplinary procedures must be followed and applied fairly, impartially, and consistently.

- Written warnings should be issued immediately to employees suspected of resident abuse.
- Staff in charge must supervise, investigate, and report irregularities according to procedure.
- Incident reports must be filed immediately after timely observation of the resident involved.
- Objective physical findings (cuts, bruises, scrapes) must be recorded on the resident's chart.
- Staff protection of any employee suspected of resident abuse may lead to additional liability.
- Inservice training is required for directors of nursing, supervisors, charge nurses, orderlies, and aides regarding the importance of documenting and reporting instances of resident abuse.

The termination of an employee who is a member of the union could result in a grievance; this could lead to arbitration or allegations of an unfair labor practice. To meet the burden of proof, the facility must have followed its established disciplinary procedure and any punishment must be reasonably related to the offense and to the employee's related past conduct. Arbitrators usually consider the extent of the facility's investigation and documentation of the employee's conduct as reflecting on the seriousness of the incident and reasonableness of the facility's findings.

Appendix 9–1
Labor Relations Glossary

Administrative law judge—Official who conducts hearings and makes recommendations to the NLRB or other governmental agency.

Adverse impact (four-fifths rule)—Under the Civil Rights Act of 1964 and its amendments, adverse impact occurs whenever the selection rate for any protected group (racial, ethnic, or gender) is less than 80 percent of the rate of selection for the nonprotected group.

Affecting commerce—Test of application of the Taft-Hartley Act. If a business is such that a labor dispute would threaten interruption of or burden interstate commerce, the jurisdiction of the NLRB comes into play.

Affirmative action—Review of hiring practices by the federal government for facility conformity to the 1964 Civil Rights Act and its amendments.

Affirmative order—Command by a labor relations board requiring persons who have engaged in unfair labor practices to take steps to undo the effect of such practices as far as possible.

Agent—Person acting for an employee or a union. An act of the agent implicates the principal in the matter of unfair labor practices or conduct subject to court action.

Arbitration—The submission for determination of a disputed matter to private, unofficial persons selected in a manner pursuant to law.

Bargaining unit—A grouping of jobs or positions in which two or more employees sharing common employment interests and conditions are entitled to select a single agent to represent them.

Boycott—Refusal to deal with or buy products of a business in order to exert pressure during a labor dispute.

Bureau of Labor Statistics—Bureau in the Labor Department that issues statistics concerning labor relations, including the consumer price index, to which some wage adjustments are tied.

Captive audience—Employees required to attend a meeting where the employer makes a speech shortly before an election. The employer is required to give the union opportunity to answer under similar circumstances where a broad no-solicitation rule is enforced.

Card check—Union authorization cards signed by employees are checked against the employer's payroll to determine if the union represents a majority of those employees.

Cease-and-desist order—Command issued by a labor relations board to require an employer or a union to abstain from unfair labor practice.

Certification—Official designation by a labor board of a labor organization entitled to bargain as exclusive representative of the employees in a bargaining unit.

Closed shop—Arrangement between an employer and union where only members of the union may be hired.

Coercion—Economic or other pressure exerted by an employer to prevent employees from self-organizing and collective bargaining. Intimidation by union or fellow employees to compel affiliation with the union.

Collective bargaining—The making of collective agreements between employers, acting through their management representative, and organized labor.

Collective bargaining contract—Formal agreement over wages, hours, and conditions of employment between a single employer or group of employers and one or more unions representing their employees.

Conciliation—When a neutral party calls the parties together, encourages communication, and serves as a procedural facilitator.

Consent election—Election held by a labor board after informal hearings where various parties agree on the terms of the election.

Cooling-off period—Period during which employees are forbidden to strike under laws that require a definite period of notification before a walkout.

Craft unit—Bargaining unit consisting of workers in a particular craft or using particular skills.

Deauthorization election—An election held by the NLRB to determine if employees wish to deprive their union bargaining agent of authority to bind them under a union-shop contract.

Decertification—Withdrawal of bargaining agent from the union upon vote by the employees in that unit that they no longer wish to be represented by the union.

Discharge—Permanent separation of employee from payroll by the employer.

Discrimination—The use of any selection procedure that has an adverse impact on hiring, promotion, or other employment or membership opportunities of members of any race, sex, or ethnic group.

Economic strike—Strike not caused by the unfair labor practice of an employer.

Employee election—Balloting by employees to choose a bargaining agent or unseating one previously recognized.

Employment contract—An agreement between an employer and one or more employees.

Fair employment practice—Conduct that does not violate the prohibition against discrimination in employment because of race, color, religion, sex, or national origin.

Free speech—The right of employers to express views against unionization, provided there is no threat of coercion or promise of benefit. Expression of coercive views is considered unlawful interference with employee rights.

Good-faith bargaining—The employer and union are required to meet at reasonable times and to confer in good faith regarding wages, hours, and other terms and conditions of employment under the Taft-Hartley Act. Neither party is required to agree to a proposal or to make a concession.

Grievance—An employee complaint. An allegation by an employee, union, or employer that a collective bargaining contract has been violated.

Individual contract—Agreement of employer with individual employee covering conditions of work.

Injunction—Mandatory order by a court to perform or cease to perform a specified unlawful activity on the grounds that the complaining party will suffer irreparable injury if this action continues.

Jurisdictional dispute—Controversy between two unions over the right to organize a group of employees or to include members employed in a specific type of work.

Labor contract—Agreement between an employer and an organization of employees covering wages, hours, and conditions of labor.

Labor dispute—Controversy between persons of the same occupation or who have an interest therein, or who work for the same employer(s), or who are members of the same union.

Layoff—Temporary dismissal of workers from their jobs.

Lockout—Closing down of a business to bring economic pressure on employees to force acceptance of the employer's terms.

Majority rule—Rule that representative chosen by the majority of employees in the bargaining unit will be the exclusive bargaining agent for that unit.

Mediation—The act of a governmental third person who interposes between parties in dispute for the purpose of reconciling them.

Open shop—Plant where employees are free to join or not join any union; opposite of union or closed shop.

Picketing—Advertising by members of a union carrying signs proclaiming the existence of a labor dispute and the union's version of its merits.

Professional employee—Employees who qualify as professional under Section 2(12) of the Taft-Hartley Act. Professionals may not be included in a unit containing nonprofessional employees unless they so elect.

Progressive discipline—Use of a specified number of oral and then more stern written warnings for each offense of the same rule before suspending or firing an employee.

Reinstatement—Return to employment of persons unlawfully discharged.

Runoff election—Second employment election directed by a labor board when the first failed to show more than half the votes recorded for any one choice.

Supervisor—An employee with authority to hire and fire or to make effective recommendations to this effect. A supervisor has no bargaining rights under the Taft-Hartley Act.

Sympathetic strike—A strike called to influence the outcome of a dispute in another industry.

Unauthorized strike—A strike by employees against or contrary to the advice of their union.

Unfair employment practice—Discrimination in employment based on race, color, religion, sex, or national origin. Forbidden by federal and some state laws.

Unfair labor practice—Practice forbidden by national or state labor relations acts.

Walkout—A strike in which workers leave the business.

CHAPTER 10

Protective Arrangements for Person and Property

The purpose of this chapter is to provide a general acquaintance with the various protective arrangements (both personal and property) for residents in long-term health care facilities. The emphasis is on protective arrangements relating to those who are healthy, incapacitated, or mentally incompetent. Briefly covered are wills and trusts dealing with property of persons who are not incapacitated or mentally incompetent; guardianships (person and property); conservatorships (property of persons who are unable to take care of themselves because of inability to manage their affairs); powers of attorney; and advance directives (persons who are mentally competent and become incompetent or incapacitated). The procedures discussed are pursuant to the Uniform Probate Code in which most states participate.

Because this material is complex, there should be no attempt to implement procedures without the assistance of an attorney conversant in probate matters. The text is not intended to give specific legal advice on probate matters but to supply basic information on the proceedings under the various protective arrangements. Language in accordance with the state statutes authorizing these arrangements must be used so that the instrument is effective and in accordance with the declarant's or principal's decisions. The documents must be witnessed as prescribed by state law. Time constraints may vary from state to state.

WILLS

The health care executive or members of the staff may be asked to witness a will or become involved in the administration of the estate of a resident. Wills are concerned with the disposition of the property of persons who are not incapacitated or mentally incompetent at the time of execution of the will; they become effective after the death of the testator. This section presents the general law and practical aspects of the procedures involved as they relate to wills.

Requirements for a Valid Will

Legal Age

The person making the will must be of legal age as required in the state statutes where the will is executed. The Uniform Probate Code indicates that any person 18 years or over who is of sound mind may make a will.

Testamentary Capacity

The testator must have a sound mind. Mere physical weakness and frailty does not mean that one is of unsound mind. The mere fact that a testator makes bequests that are considered foolish, unusual, or unjust does not affect his or her testamentary capacity.

> In *Patterson v. Imbsen*, 194 NW 842, the court said, in effect, that the soundness of mind does not necessarily mean the degree of intellectual vigor enjoyed in youth. For the purposes of making a will, one who has a sound mind is one who, without prompting, has intelligent knowledge of the act engaged in, has full knowledge of the property he or she possesses, is capable of understanding the disposition he or she wishes to make, is also capable of knowing the persons that he or she desires to be recipients of his or her gifts, and can recollect and apprehend the nature of the claims of those who are excluded from participating in these gifts.

Duress, Fraud, and Undue Influence

The testator must be free from duress, fraud, or undue influence when making a will. **Duress** is the threatening to do bodily harm in order to coerce the terms of the will—for example, a type of duress occurs when a person holds a gun to the head of a testator and instructs him or her to leave this person a bequest under the will. **Fraud** is a deceitful practice or willful device to deceive one so that he or she will act in a certain way—for example, using a deceitful practice to gain an advantage from the testator. **Undue influence** is an act whereby the freedom of another is destroyed and the mind of the person committing this undue influence is substituted for the mind of the testator.

> In *Re Kolland Estate*, 18 NW 2d 290, the court indicated that the following elements must be present to invalidate a will on the basis of undue influence: the testator must be susceptible to such undue influence, the opportunity to exert such influence must be present, a disposition must be drawn up indicating the intent to do so for an improper purpose, and the result must clearly show the effect of such influence.

Witnesses

Any adult person generally competent to be a witness may act as a witness to a will. According to the Uniform Probate Code, a will or any provision thereof is not invalidated because the will is witnessed by an interested party; however, this is not the law in some states.

Execution of a Will

The health care executive or his or her staff are not qualified to draw up wills. However, there may be occasions where residents approach death quickly and wish to execute wills. Consultation with an attorney is recommended; there are words in wills that have special legal meanings and, if used incorrectly, may be the source of litigation. The following material is intended to provide general information on the execution of wills.

The manner in which a will is made is spelled out in the Uniform Probate Code or in a particular state statute. Generally,

- All of the witnesses and the testator should be present together during the process of executing the will.
- The will should be in writing, preferably typewritten.
- The testator should sign the will. If he or she cannot sign it because of sickness or infirmity, another person may sign at the testator's request and in the testator's presence. Ordinarily, the signature of the testator is at the end of the will. However, there is no requirement that this be the case; if a testator writes his or her name in the body of the will with

the intent of its being his or her signature, the requirement of the statute is satisfied.

- The subscribing witnesses sign the will and observe the testator and other witnesses signing the will. States participating in the Uniform Probate Code require at least two witnesses for the will to be valid.
- The testator may sign the will outside the presence of the witnesses if he or she later acknowledges to the witnesses that the signature is his or hers and that the document is his or her will.
- Quite often, a witness to a will may be considered the most qualified individual to testify as to the testamentary capacity of the testator. Thus, the witness to a will should be familiar with the testator, particularly in the nursing facility situation. It is recommended that when a will is executed in the health care facility, a notation be made in the testator's health record indicating his or her mental condition at the time of the execution of the will.
- After the will is executed, it should be placed in a safe place—for example, the facility's safe, the office of the attorney drafting the will, or a safe deposit box at a financial institution. A court order may be necessary to get into a safe deposit box at a bank or other financial institution after the testator's death.

Revocation of a Will

A duly executed will remains valid until it is revoked. There are several ways in which a will or any part thereof is revoked.

- by a subsequent will that revokes the prior will or parts thereof, expressly or by inconsistency
- by being burned, canceled, obliterated, or destroyed with intent and for the purpose of revoking it by the testator or at his or her direction
- as it relates to the former spouse after the testator is divorced or his or her marriage annulled

Probate of a Will

The long-term care facility executive should also be familiar with the general steps in the probate of a will from the time of the death of a person until final accounting. The steps may vary from one state to another; following is a general procedure for the probate of a will:

1. Most states require that the person holding the will of the decedent deliver the will to the court having probate jurisdiction within 30 days after the death of the decedent.
2. A petition (request) to this court must be made and include the names and addresses of the heirs, the character and value of the estate, and the name and address of the person named as executor or executrix. The will is usually attached to the petition.
3. The judge fixes a day to hear the petition.
4. A notice of the hearing must be published generally once a week for three successive weeks. A copy of the notice must be mailed to all the persons taking under the will. Publication of the notice of hearing is necessary to inform creditors of the estate and the heirs, in the event they wish to contest the will.
5. Any person who is interested may appear at the hearing and object to the probate of the will. To contest the will, it is generally required that written grounds be furnished and a copy mailed to the representative of the estate and all other interested parties.
6. The court may have the attesting witnesses to the will appear at the hearing; they are questioned by the attorney about the testamentary capacity of the deceased, whether or not the signing was a voluntary act, and whether or not the execution was proper and according to law. If no one at the hearing contests the will, it is usually admitted to probate.
7. At this time, the oath of the executor or executrix of the estate is given. Not all persons qualify as an executor or executrix of a will. These persons must have obtained the age of majority, must not have been convicted of an infamous crime, and must not be judged incompetent by reason of drunkenness, imprudence, or want of understanding or integrity.
8. Letters testamentary are issued to the executor or executrix so that he or she has the legal authority to properly distribute the property of the decedent. A bond is executed unless the will indicates that no bond is necessary. A special checking account is usually opened for the liquid assets of the estate to pay for valid claims against the estate. An appraisal of the inventory of the estate must be signed by the appraisers under oath.

9. The executor or executrix collects all assets and prepares them for distribution. If the decedent is survived by a spouse or minor children, homestead and family allowances may be made. All creditors of the decedent must submit claims to the court within four months (this time varies with state law) after the date of the first publication of the notice or be forever barred. The payment of the creditors must follow according to state statute; generally, the priority of payment is as follows:
   a. expenses of the administrator
   b. expenses of last sickness
   c. funeral expenses
   d. any debt to employees
   e. debts having preference by the laws of the United States
   f. all other demands against the estate
10. When all taxes, creditors, and other debts are paid, the attorney handling the administration of the estate may petition for the distribution of the estate.
11. After the estate is distributed to the legatees in accordance with the will, the executor or executrix makes a final accounting and settlement of the will.
12. When the estate is fully administered and it is shown by the executor or executrix that all money due has been paid and all property in the will distributed to the legatees, the court issues a decree discharging the executor or executrix from all liabilities and from his or her duties.

TRUSTS

A trust is any arrangement whereby real or personal property is transferred with the intention that it be held or administered by a trustee for another's use or benefit. The trustee has an obligation to administer the property for the benefit of the third party according to the terms of the trust. The trust takes effect in accordance with its specific terms after it is properly created and terminates, generally, according to its terms. There are many forms of trusts.

Creation of a Trust

To have the capacity to transfer property in trust, the person must have reached the age of majority, be mentally competent, and be the owner of the property to be transferred.

It is common practice to execute a written document, referred to as a *trust agreement* or *deed of trust*, when creating a trust. Generally, no particular form of language is necessary as long as the property, the purpose of the trust, and the beneficiaries are designated. Other requirements include:

- If the trust is created by the will of the settlor, the trust agreement must meet the requirements of the will.
- The statute of frauds requires that the details of any interest in land be evidenced in the trust agreement where a inter vivos (living) trust is involved.
- An intention to impose a duty on the trustee with respect to the specific property must be expressed.
- An active duty must be placed on the trustee to manage the property in some specific manner or to exercise his or her discretion or judgment.
- Because the performance of a trust imposes a burden upon the trustee, he or she cannot be required to serve as trustee against his or her will. He or she may renounce or reject the trust. Such renunciation does not affect the validity of the trust; the court will appoint a substitute trustee if the settlor does not.
- Every trust must have a beneficiary. In a private trust, the beneficiary must be identified by name, description, or designation of the specific class to which he or she belongs. In a charitable trust, it is sufficient that the beneficiaries be members of the public at large or a general class of the public.

Termination of a Trust

A trust may be terminated under several conditions.

- in accordance with its terms
- because of the impossibility of obtaining the objectives of the trust
- by revocation by the settlor, when allowed by the terms of the trust
- by merger of all interests in the same person
- upon the request of all the beneficiaries when there is no expressed purpose that requires a continuation of the trust

Duties of the Trustee

A trustee is under the duty to carry out the trust according to its terms and cannot delegate the performance of his or her personal duties unless otherwise provided by the terms of the trust. In dealing with the trust assets, the trustee must observe those standards of due care that would be observed by a prudent person when dealing with the property of another. If the trustee has special skills or was named trustee on the basis of special skills or expertise, he or she is under a duty to employ those skills in the administration of the trust.

A trustee need not provide bond to secure performance of the duties unless required to do so by the terms of the trust or by a beneficiary or by the court as reasonably necessary to protect the interest of beneficiaries who are unable to protect themselves and whose interests are otherwise not adequately represented. If required, a bond is filed in the appropriate court in the amounts and with the sureties and liabilities as provided therein.

A trustee is not permitted to profit personally from this position other than to receive the compensation allowed by contract or by law. He or she is under a duty to take possession of the trust property and preserve it from loss or damage. Any accounts receivable or outstanding debts must be collected. The money or property must be invested in enterprises or transactions that will yield income to the estate in accordance with ex-pressed or implied direction.

The trustee must keep accurate records to document that the trust was properly administered and must furnish any information with respect to the trust upon request by the beneficiaries. A beneficiary is entitled to a statement of the trust accounts annually, upon termination of the trust, or on a change of trustee. Periodically, at times determined by state law, the trustee must file an accounting in court, at which time the court passes upon the trust stewardship.

A trustee is entitled to compensation. It is common to stipulate specific compensation expressed in terms of percentages of the principal or income amounts administered by the trustee. A statute or court prescribes the percentage amount in some states. In absence of any controlling provision, the court where the trustee files the account awards the compensation it determines reasonable for the services rendered.

CONSERVATORSHIPS

A conservatorship provides protection for the property of protected persons. Under the Uniform Probate Code, a protected person is a minor or other person for whom a conservator has been appointed or other protective order made as to the management of his or her property. This appointment is made in relation to the estate and affairs of a person whom the court has determined to be unable to manage his or her property and affairs effectively for reasons such as mental illness, advanced age, or chronic use of drugs or alcohol, and whose property will be wasted or dissipated unless proper management is provided or whose funds are needed for the support, care, and welfare of those entitled to his or her support.

Who May Be a Conservator

The court may appoint the following as conservator of the estate of a protected person:

- an individual or a corporation with general powers to serve as trustee
- in accordance with the protected person's most recent nomination in a durable power of attorney
- an individual or corporation nominated by the protected person, if the protected person is 14 years of age or older and has sufficient mental capacity to make an intelligent choice
- the spouse of the protected person
- an adult child of the protected person
- a parent of the protected person or a person nominated by the will of a deceased parent
- any relative of the protected person with whom the protected person has lived for more than six months prior to the filing of the petition
- a person nominated by another who is caring for or paying benefits to the protected person

Court Appointment of a Conservator

A petition for the appointment of a conservator may be made to the court by the person to be protected; anyone interested in his or her estate, affairs, or welfare (including his or her parent, guardian, or custodian); or any person adversely affected by lack of effective management of his or her property and affairs. The interest of the petitioner; the name, age, and address of the person to be protected; the name and address of the guardian (if any); the name and address of his or her nearest relative known to the petitioner, a general statement of his or her property with estimated value; and the reason why the appointment of a conservator is necessary must all be set forth in the petition itself.

A notice of the proceeding at least 14 days (this period may vary from state to state) before the date of the hearing must be served personally upon the person to be protected and the spouse or parents (if no spouse). Waiver by the person to be protected is not effective unless he or she attends the hearing.

By accepting appointment, a conservator submits personally to the jurisdiction of the court in proceedings instituted by any interested person relating to the estate. Interested persons may include heirs, devisees, children, spouses, creditors, beneficiaries, and any others having a property right in or claim against a trust estate or the estate of a decedent, ward, or protected person that may be affected by the proceeding.

Any visitor, lawyer, physician, conservator, or special conservator appointed in a protective proceeding is entitled to reasonable compensation from the estate if not otherwise compensated for services.

General Powers of the Conservator

The court may require a conservator to furnish a bond conditioned upon faithful discharge of all duties of the trust according to law.

Within 90 days after an appointment, the conservator must prepare and file with the appointing court a complete inventory of the estate of the protected person together with any oath or affirmation that it is complete and accurate so far as he or she is informed.

Every conservator must account to the court for his or her administration of the trust as indicated by the court and upon resignation or removal.

Some of the powers of a conservator are to:

- Collect, hold, and retain the estate assets; invest and reinvest the estate assets; deposit funds in the bank; acquire or dispose of assets, including land.
- Continue or participate in the operation of any business or enterprise.
- Make ordinary or extraordinary repairs or alterations in buildings or other structures.

- Enter into a lease agreement for any purpose.
- Vote a security in person or by general or limited proxy.
- Borrow money to be repaid by the estate assets or otherwise.
- Pay or contest any claim or settle a claim by or against the estate and prosecute or defend actions against the estate.
- Pay taxes, assessments, compensation of the conservator, and other expenses.
- Employ persons, including attorneys, auditors, investment advisors, and agents.
- Execute and deliver all instruments that will accomplish or facilitate the exercise of powers invested in the conservator.

Termination of Conservatorship

The protected person, his or her personal representative, the conservator, or any other interested person may petition the court to terminate the conservatorship. Upon termination, title to the assets of the estate passes to the former protected person or to his or her successor.

GUARDIANSHIPS

The long-term care facility executive may be called upon to take care of (or assist a relative to take care of) the property and person of a resident who is no longer able to care for his or her property or person. Generally, a guardian is a person who is given the legal power and charged with the duty of taking care of the person and managing the property rights of someone who, because of defect of age, status, understanding, or self-control, is unable to administer his or her own estate or take care of him or herself.

Who May Be a Guardian

Any competent adult or suitable institution may be appointed guardian of an incapacitated person, with priority for appointment as follows:

1. the spouse
2. an adult child
3. a parent, including a person nominated by a will or other writing signed by a deceased parent
4. any relative with whom the incapacitated person has resided for more than six months prior to the filing of the petition
5. a person nominated by and caring for or paying benefit to the person who is unable to care for him- or herself or his or her property

Court Appointment of a Guardian

There must be a court order appointing a person to be a legal, general, or special guardian. The court appoints a guardian, if requested, when it is satisfied that the person for whom the guardian is sought is incapacitated and that the appointment is necessary and desirable to provide him or her with continuing care and supervision. Guardians appointed by will give a bond and receive letters of guardianship. The court usually has the power to appoint a guardian over the person and/or estate if the person is shown to have an unsound mind or is a recipient of public welfare, wasteful, and unable to manage the money received from the public welfare. General procedure is as follows:

1. The incapacitated person, a relative, or any person interested in his or her welfare may file a petition for a finding of incapacity and appointment of a guardian. The reason for guardianship must be clearly stated in the petition.
2. After the petition is filed, the court sets the date for a hearing regarding the need for and the qualifications of the guardian. At this time, the court appoints an appropriate attorney to represent the allegedly incapacitated person during the proceedings if he or she does not have counsel of choice.
3. The allegedly incapacitated person is examined by a court-appointed physician, who submits a written report to the court.
4. The court also sends a visitor to interview the allegedly incapacitated person and the person seeking appointment as guardian. The visitor need not be a lawyer; he or she may be a social worker capable of determining the needs of the allegedly incapacitated person. The visitor visits the present residence and the proposed residence of the allegedly incapacitated person and submits a written report to the court.

5. The allegedly incapacitated person is entitled to be present physically or by counsel at the hearing. He or she is entitled to hear and see all evidence relating to his or her condition, present evidence, and cross-examine witnesses, including the court-appointed physician and visitor. The issue of incapacity may be determined at a closed hearing without a jury if so requested by the allegedly incapacitated person or his or her counsel or by a trial by jury, where permitted by state law.

6. If the court is convinced of the need for a guardianship, letters of guardianship are issued. The court often specifies directions for the care of the protected person and/or the management of the estate. By accepting appointment, the guardian personally submits to the jurisdiction of the court in proceedings instituted by any interested party relating to the guardianship. Notice of any proceeding is delivered to the guardian or mailed to him or her by ordinary mail at the address listed in the court records.

General Powers of a Guardian

A guardian is responsible for the ward's support, health, and education, having the same powers, rights, and duties as a parent has respecting his or her unemancipated minor child. The relationship of the guardian and ward is confidential. A legal obligation of trust is required for the guardian. He or she is answerable to the court for maintaining the property without waste, collection of debts and settlement of payment for all legal debts received in maintaining health and support, conduct of any related litigation, and settling tort claims. A guardian has the following powers and duties:

• The guardian is entitled to the custody of the person of his or her ward and may establish the ward's place of residence within or without a state. He or she provides for the care, comfort, training, and education, where appropriate, and maintenance of the ward. The guardian gives necessary consents or approvals to enable medical or other professional care, counsel, treatment, or service.

• The guardian takes reasonable care of his or her ward's clothing, furniture, vehicles, and other personal effects. He or she may receive money and tangible property deliverable to the ward directly and use such items for the support, care, and education of the ward. He or she may commence any protective proceedings, if required, regarding other property.

- If no conservator for the ward's estate is appointed, the guardian may institute proceedings to compel any person under a duty to pay reasonable sums for his or her services and the welfare and/or support of the ward. If a conservator is appointed, the guardian may request that the conservator expend the ward's estate by payment, for care of the ward, to a third person or institution.
- The guardian is required by the court to report the condition of his or her ward and the related estate, usually annually.

Termination of Guardianship

The authority and responsibilities for an incapacitated or incompetent person terminate upon the death of the guardian or ward, a determination of incapacity on the part of the guardian, resignation, if deemed proper, by the court, or removal by the court if the guardian:

- Abuses his or her trust.
- Is incapable, fails to perform, or has an interest that is adverse to the performance of his or her duties.
- Is convicted of gross immorality.
- Moves from a state where the ward legally resides.

If an incapacitated person has no guardian and an emergency exists, the court may act as guardian pending notice and hearing. The court may appoint a temporary guardian for a specified period of time (usually not to exceed six months) if an appointed guardian is not performing his or her duties and the welfare of the incapacitated person requires immediate attention. The authority of the previous guardian is suspended as long as the temporary guardian has authority. The temporary guardian must report as the court requires and may be removed at any time.

ADVANCE DIRECTIVES AND INFORMED CONSENT

The Patient Self-Determination Act of 1990 (PSDA-90) mandates that health care facilities accepting Medicare and Medicaid funds from the federal government assure individuals upon admission to the facility that they have the right to participate in and to direct the health care decisions that affect them.

Federal regulations (42 CFR, Sec 489.102, Ch. IV, 10-1-98) define advance directives as written instruments, such as living wills or durable powers of attorney for health care, relating to the provision of health care when an individual is incapacitated. These are recognized under state law or by the state courts.

Skilled nursing facilities are among those health care providers that must maintain written policies and procedures concerning advance directives with regard to all adult residents. Facilities are required to provide written information at the time of admission regarding:

- The right under state law to make decisions concerning medical care, refuse medical or surgical treatment, and formulate an advance directive. If state law changes, the facility must inform the resident within 90 days.
- The facility's written policies to implement these rights and a clear, precise statement concerning any limitation to implementation on the basis of conscientious objection, including the:
  - difference between the institutionwide conscientious objections and those of individual physicians
  - state legal authority allowing such objections
  - medical conditions or procedures covered
- Documentation in residents' medical records as to whether or not the individual has executed an advance directive.

Facilities must also

- Ensure compliance with state law (statutory or recognition by the courts).
- Educate staff concerning facility policy and procedure in this area.
- Provide (or participate with other providers or organizations) for community education, including the what, why, and state laws involved. Written materials may be developed. Documentation of community education efforts is required.

This advance directive information is given to the family, surrogate, or other concerned persons (under state law) should the individual be incapacitated at the time of admission. Follow-up procedure must ensure that such a resident is directly informed once he or she is no longer incapacitated.

Facilities are not to provide care that conflicts with an advance directive. They are not required to implement an advance directive if there is an institutionwide conscientious objection and state law allows such objection.

Under the presumption of sweetness and light, every individual is deemed to be competent unless adjudicated by a court of law to be otherwise. Thus, an individual has the right to be informed about his or her medical care, to accept or refuse medical or surgical treatment, and to communicate wishes concerning present treatment and future treatment by prior selection of a person to make health care decisions in the event of his or her incapacity or incompetence. Legal instruments recognized under state law for implementing PSDA-90 include informed consent, living wills, and durable powers of attorney for health care. Brief explanations follow.

If there is no advance directive for health care, the attending physician, with the advice and consent of the family or next of kin, tries to make medical care decisions based on what he or she feels is best for the incapacitated or incompetent person, taking into account any known wishes. Many states have statutes that outline the priority followed in picking someone to act for the incapacitated or incompetent person. This order is usually spouse, adult children, father or mother, brother or sister.

Where advance directives are executed in compliance with state law, the following principles may apply in accordance with specific state law:

- An attending physician or health care provider who is unable to comply with an advance directive must take reasonable action to transfer the declarant or principal to another physician or facility. Willful failure to transfer under these conditions may result in a criminal action. Most religious faiths approve of the individual's choice to make advance directives.
- No one may prohibit the making of advance directives as a precondition for being insured to receive health care services.
- Advance directives do not condone, authorize, or approve mercy killing, euthanasia, or suicide.
- Life insurance policies are not impaired, modified, or invalidated by the execution of advance directives.

- A physician ordering, or a person participating in, the withholding or withdrawing of life-sustaining procedures in accordance with advance directives and state law is not subject to civil or criminal liability or charges of unprofessional conduct.
- Death resulting from the withdrawal or withholding of life-sustaining procedures does not constitute suicide or homicide.

Informed Consent

Informed consent ensures that an individual, guardian, or agent receives adequate and full information to make a knowledgeable decision as a competent adult concerning any proposed medical or surgical treatment before agreeing to proceed with that treatment.

To give or withhold informed consent, the following information must be provided by the attending physician or other personnel of the health care facility as a minimum:

1. The nature and purpose of the proposed treatment or procedure. The caregiver must explain the steps involved and the diagnostic or therapeutic results that are sought.
2. The risks and likelihood of success of the treatment or procedure.
3. Any alternative courses of treatment, including the option of no treatment (informed refusal).

PSDA-90 ensures that the individual has the right to give or withhold consent for any medical or surgical procedure. Part of an informed consent includes the right to decide personal quality of life and whether or not to employ artificial life support systems where there is no reasonable hope of getting better.

Living Will

A living will is concerned with personal health care decisions. This document (see Exhibit 10–1 for an example) gives precise instructions to the attending physician and health care provider (hospital, nursing facility, etc.) directing the life-sustaining medical treatment desired or not desired in the event of incapacity and a terminal condition or illness. The form and validity of living wills are covered by statutory law, which may vary from state to state.

This written document may control life or death and becomes effective when signed by a competent adult 18 years or older, usually in the presence of two subscribing witnesses, and copies are given to the attending physician and health care providers. Copies are also often given to the declarant's attorney, clergyperson, and family members. The living will must become part of the declarant's medical record. It becomes operative when the attending physician makes a determination of a terminal illness or condition (as prescribed by state law) and the declarant is incompetent and/or incapacitated.

The living will remains valid and in effect until revoked by the declarant. It may be amended or revoked at any time by notifying the attending physician and health care providers of the changes or revocation; a notation to this effect is made in the medical record. Periodic review (every two years) ensures that this instrument continues to reflect the principal's wishes.

It is important to note that the living will is not operative when the declarant becomes unable to make health care decisions unless he or she is also determined by a physician in accordance with state law to have a terminal condition or disease. It also does not deal with the many health care decisions other than life-sustaining treatment that must be made should the principal become incapacitated or incompetent and/or terminally ill.

General Power of Attorney

A power of attorney is a legal device that permits one individual (the principal) to give another person (the attorney in fact or agent) authority to act on his or her behalf. The agent need not be a lawyer and may be a spouse, adult child, brother or sister, best friend, or close associate. When the power given to the agent is very broad, it is most important to select an individual whom the principal trusts. A power of attorney can authorize the agent to do all manner of things—receive and deposit assets, sign contracts, buy or sell real or personal property, sue or be sued, make gifts, establish trusts, spend income from trust, and, in short, act on a wide range of legal matters. On the other hand, the authority given can be narrow and limited in both time and scope. Such powers of attorney are granted to real estate agents or stockbrokers, where the power is given only to offer or make an offer on property at a given price for a specific period of time.

The theory behind the power of attorney is that it is renewed each and every moment during its existence, thus requiring that the maker of the power have the mental capacity to renew this constant power. If no time limit is set forth, the power of attorney continues indefinitely as long as the principal lives, is competent, is capable of granting that power, and does not expressly and specifically revoke the power of attorney.

Therefore, if the principal should fall into a coma or otherwise become mentally incompetent, the power of attorney automatically expires. In terms of protective arrangements, this means that the power of attorney disappears when the principal becomes incapacitated and unable to act on his or her own behalf, just at the time when he or she needs someone who can act on his or her behalf.

Durable Power of Attorney

A durable power of attorney deals with the decisions a person wishes to have carried out should he or she become incapacitated. It is drawn up so that another person (agent or attorney in fact) can make health care decisions and/or conduct business matters should the principal become unable to do so. Prior to the development of this special legal device, when an individual became unable to manage his or her property or person, it was necessary for someone to petition the court for appointment of a guardian or conservator to make these decisions. Another possibility was for a competent individual to create a funded revocable trust and transfer title of his or her property to someone to manage during any periods of incapacity or incapacitation; this, however, may or may not take care of decisions about one's person or health care. The Uniform Durable Power of Attorney Act provided an alternative for court-oriented procedures, such as conservatorship, guardianship, and funded revocable trusts.

The durable power of attorney is a device, authorized by state statute, under which the principal, while competent, expresses his or her intent concerning the durability of his or her power through an agent to survive any incapacitation or incompetency. The document itself must contain a statement such as "This power of attorney shall not be affected by subsequent disability or incapacity of the principal" or "This power of attorney shall become effective upon the incapacity or incompetency of the principal" to be valid and to show the intent of the principal that the authority given to another can be used if the principal is unable to act for him- or herself.

A power of attorney that becomes effective only upon the incapacity and/or incompetency of the principal is termed *springing power*. An advantage of a springing power is that it leaves the principal, while competent and able, in complete and sole control of his or her property and person, as the agent cannot act. However, while one is competent and capable, there still may be difficulty in going to the bank, writing checks, or otherwise conducting business; it is sometimes necessary to appoint someone with the power to perform these functions.

Questions may arise concerning just when the principal becomes incompetent or incapacitated and when this power really comes into being. This determination is generally made by the attending physician.

The execution of a durable power of attorney including health care should be undertaken with care. It seems that the powers provided to an agent might be likened to those of a trustee, guardian, or conservator. Although considerable power is put into the hands of the agent, he or she has a duty to obey the will of the principal and to act in accordance with the principal's expressed wishes or with what he or she understood the principal's wishes would be under the particular circumstances. The agent may have powers, if expressly set forth in the instrument, that permit the making of gifts, creation of a trust, disclaimer of interested property, changing of beneficiaries under insurance and annuity policies, and direction as to artificial life-support systems and artificial hydration or nutrition.

The powers granted to an agent last indefinitely, for a certain number of years as determined by state law, or may be limited within the document itself. However, the durable power of attorney can be revoked orally or in writing at any time as long as the principal is a competent adult and acts in accordance with state statute. At the point of incompetency or incapacity, the principal is unable to undo what he or she has done. Review of the durable power of attorney is usually recommended every few years to check that the decisions made are still appropriate.

The execution of a durable power of attorney does not mean that a guardian might not be appointed subsequently by the court. The principal may nominate his or her guardian in the durable power in the event of incompetency proceedings. The relationship of the agent to the guardian is the same as that of the agent to the principal; the guardian has the power to terminate the durable power of attorney. It is likely that the material and information in the durable power would be given great weight by any guardian the court may appoint.

Durable Power of Attorney for Health Care

There was some controversy as to whether or not durable powers of attorney should permit agents to make health care decisions. Because courts look for collateral material that assists in making health care decisions (to give or withhold consent for treatment, for participation in research, for resuscitation or no-resuscitation orders, and similar matters), great consideration is given to any expressions of intent that could guide future guardians, family members, and agents where such expressions are included within the durable power of attorney. States have enacted right-to-die (living will) statutes and legislation permitting the appointment of a health care representative to give or withhold consent for medical care when an individual is no longer capable of doing so him- or herself. Great weight is given by courts, physicians, caregivers, and agents to a document that lays out explicit guidelines to follow in the event health care decisions are required.

A durable power of attorney for health care is a document appointing another person to make health care decisions should the principal become incapacitated and no longer capable of making such decisions. The preceding discussion on durable power of attorney also applies to this special durable power.

A durable power of attorney for health care may be written in broad terms entirely or with part of it in broad language and other parts in more specific language (see Exhibits 10–2 through 10–4). A well-drawn power of attorney for health care can include directives as to artificial life-support systems and artificial hydration or nutrition, eliminating the need for a separate living will. If there is a separate living will, reference should be made to it in the durable power of attorney for health care.

When selecting an agent, it is very important that the principal discuss his or her philosophy related to quality of life and wishes concerning artificial life-support systems and other medical decisions (including whether or not there is to be any medical intervention whatsoever), should severe illness develop. The principal should select someone who knows him or her best and in whom he or she has confidence to carry out the activities regarding necessary health care decisions should he or she become unable to do so. The principal should consider where the prospective agent lives and whether or not he or she can be present when the health care decisions need to be made. An alternative agent may be named to act in the event that the first choice is unavailable. The agent must follow expressed wishes concerning the principal's health care decisions and must consider the physician's recommendations. Any decision by the appointed agent must be in accordance with accepted medical practice. Limiting the authority of the agent and the term of years may help keep the principal's decisions current in view of a drastic change in his or her medical situation or development of a severe illness.

The original power of attorney for health care should be kept in a safe place and copies given to the attending physician, health care providers (nursing facility, hospital, etc.), designated agent, trusted family member, and clergyperson. All copies should be replaced when this instrument is amended or revoked.

Appendix 10–1
Protective Arrangements Glossary

Advance directive—A written instrument (such as a living will or durable power of attorney for health care) given by a competent adult to his or her agent, to become operative in the event of incapacity or incompetency.

Attending physician—The physician who has primary responsibility for the treatment and care of the resident/patient.

Attorney in fact/agent—The person appointed to act on one's behalf to make medical decisions.

Beneficiary—The person for whose benefit the trustee holds the property.

Charitable trust—Trust created for the benefit of the public or certain classes of the public.

Codicil—An addition to a will that explains, modifies, or changes the will or part of it.

Contest of a will—A legal proceeding concerning the eligibility of admitting a will to probate or concerning the validity of the will.

Decedent—A person who dies with or without a will.

Declarant—A competent adult who executes a living will governing the withholding or withdrawing of life-sustaining treatment.

Devise—A testamentary disposition (a witnessed statement under oath) of real and/or personal property taking place under a will.

Devisee—Any person designated in the will to receive a devise.

Durable power of attorney for health care—A legal document where the principal appoints an agent to make all types of health care decisions if and when the principal becomes incapable of making them. A health care proxy is used in states where there are no laws covering durable power of attorney for health care.

Execution—Carrying out an act to completion—that is, the making and signing of a will.

Guardian—A person who has legal power and duty to take and manage the person and property of another person pursuant to testamentary appointment (named in a will) or by court appointment. Some types of guardians are:

- *Domestic guardian*—Appointed within the state in which the protected person resides.
- *Foreign guardian*—Appointed by the courts of another state. Usually has charge of only such property within the state where legally residing.
- *General guardian*—Has the general care and control of the person and his or her estate.
- *Guardian ad litum*—Appointed by a court to prosecute or defend a minor in any suit where he or she is a party.
- *Natural guardian*—The biological mother or father of a child.
- *Special guardian*—Has special or limited powers and duties concerning custody of the estate but not of the person. Some states call this person a *conservator*.

Health care provider—A person or institution licensed, certified, or otherwise authorized by state law to administer health care in the ordinary course of business practice or profession.

Hydration and nutrition—Involves the use of tubes carrying special vitamin solutions inserted into a vein, through the nose into the stomach, or, surgically, directly into the stomach.

Incapacitated—Any condition where an individual cannot communicate.

Incapacitated person—Anyone who is impaired by reason of mental illness or deficiency, physical illness or disability, advanced age, chronic use of drugs, chronic intoxication, or other cause to the extent that he or she lacks sufficient understanding or capacity to make or communicate responsible decisions concerning his or her person.

Incompetent—A determination by a court that an individual is incapable of acting on his or her own behalf.

Inter vivos trust (living trust)—Trust created to take effect during the lifetime of the settlor.

Intestate—Without making a will.

Intestate succession—Historically called *descent and distribution*, this is the method whereby property is distributed when a person dies without making a valid will. Each state has intestate laws that specifically describe the manner in which the property or assets are disposed. The most common pattern for descent and distribution is:

- A larger share is given to the surviving spouse if there are issue (children) or the whole estate if there are no issue or parents.
- An heir must survive the decedent for five days in order to take under the statute.
- Adopted children are treated as children of the adopting parents for all inheritance purposes and cease to be children of the natural parents.
- Gifts during a lifetime are not considered advancements unless so declared or acknowledged in writing.
- A surviving spouse, heir, or devisee who feloniously and intentionally kills the decedent is not entitled to any benefits as a joint tenant or beneficiary under the will by intestate distribution.

Joint tenancy property—Property owned jointly by two individuals. Upon the death of one of the joint tenants, the surviving tenant has total ownership.

Legacy—A bequest of personal or real property given by means of a will. A general legacy is money paid out to the general assets of the estate. A specific legacy is a bequest of a particular thing—a car, house, or boat, for example.

Life-sustaining treatment—Involves various medical procedures or interventions to maintain life when an organ or body system does not function properly so a person can survive. Hydration and nutrition are not included; treatments do include:

- *artificial ventilation or respiration*—a procedure maintaining respiration by manual or mechanical means when normal breathing has stopped
- *cardiopulmonary resuscitation (CPR)*—a procedure helping the heart to function again after it has stopped beating
- *kidney dialysis (hemodialysis)*—a procedure removing impurities or waste from the blood

Living will—A document that gives precise instructions directly to a physician directing the life-sustaining treatment a person wishes to receive or not to receive in the event of a terminal illness or condition and inability to participate in medical decisions.

Personal property—Property of a personal nature—cars, boats, jewelry, and household goods, for example.

Principal—A person appointing an agent to act for him or her under certain circumstances.

Private trust—Trust created for the benefit of private individuals.

Probate matters—Having to do with the handling of estates.

Protective proceeding—A proceeding to determine that a person cannot effectively manage or apply his or her estate to necessary ends because he or she either lacks the ability or is otherwise inconvenienced.

Real property—Land and that which is attached or affixed to the land.

Settlor or donor—The owner who creates the trust.

Subscribing witness—A person who witnesses or attests to the signature of a testator and who signs his or her own name to the document in the presence of the testator.

Supportive care—Care given to provide comfort, dignity, and hygiene but not to prolong life. The use of medication to relieve pain is one type of supportive care.

Terminal illness or condition—An incurable or irreversible condition that, without the administration of life-sustaining procedures, will result in death within a short or foreseeable but uncertain time, in the opinion of the attending physician.

Testacy proceeding—A proceeding to establish a will or to determine intestacy.

Testamentary capacity—The determination as to whether a person has sufficient mental capacity to make a will.

> In *In Re Larson Estate*, 71 P 2d 47, the court said, in effect, that a testator, to have such capacity, must have sufficient mind and memory to intelligently understand the nature of his or her business, to know, in general, the extent and nature of his or her property, and to know who is to receive his or her bequests.

Testamentary trust—Trust provided for in the settlor's will; becomes effective only when the will takes effect after death.

Testator—One who makes a valid will.

Trust corpus, fund, or estate—The property that is held in trust. This property is sometimes referred to as the *principal*. The income earned by this principal is distributed by the trustee in accordance with the trust agreement.

Trustee—The person to whom the property is transferred.

Ward or protected person—A minor or incapacitated person for whom a guardian or conservator has been appointed by a court.

Will—The statement of a person regarding the manner in which he or she wishes to give his or her property to someone. It takes effect and is carried out after his or her death.

- A *general will* is typed, properly attested, and executed.
- A *holographic will* is entirely written in the testator's handwriting and is dated and signed by the testator.
- A *nuncupative will* is an oral declaration by a person wishing to make a will in his or her last sickness (or in an emergency) before a sufficient number of witnesses and later reduced to writing.
- A *joint will* is an instrument made and signed by two or more persons. This kind of will is used to dispose of joint property.
- A *mutual will* is one where two or more persons make mutual provisions in favor of each other. These wills may be executed in two separate or included in one instrument.

Appendix 10–2
Exhibits

Exhibit 10–1 Living Will Example

This sample of a living will is provided for informational purposes only. It complies with South Dakota law, SDCL 34-12-D3.

I, _____ , willfully and voluntarily make this declaration as a directive to be followed if I am in a terminal condition and become unable to participate in decisions regarding my medical care.

With respect to any life-sustaining treatment, I direct the following. [Initial only the options with which you agree.] If you do not agree with any of the following, space is provided below to write your own directive.

_____ NO LIFE-SUSTAINING TREATMENT—I direct that no life-sustaining treatment be provided. If life-sustaining treatment is begun, terminate it.

_____ TREATMENT FOR RESTORATION—Provide life-sustaining treatment only if and for as long as you believe treatment offers a reasonable possibility of restoring to me the ability to think and act for myself.

_____ TREAT UNLESS PERMANENTLY UNCONSCIOUS—If you believe that I am permanently unconscious and are satisfied that this condition is irreversible, then do not provide me with life-sustaining treatment, and if life-sustaining treatment is being provided to me, terminate it. If and as long as you believe that treatment has a reasonable possibility of restoring consciousness to me, then provide life-sustaining treatment.

_____ MAXIMUM TREATMENT—Preserve my life as long as possible, but do not provide treatment that is not in accordance with accepted medical standards as then in effect.

[Artificial nutrition and hydration is food and water provided by means of a nasogastric tube or tube inserted into the stomach, intestines, or veins. If you do not wish to receive this form of treatment, you must initial the statement below that reads "I intend to include this treatment among the life-sustaining treatments that may be withheld or withdrawn."]

continues

Exhibit 10–1 continued

With respect to ARTIFICIAL NUTRITION AND HYDRATION, I wish to make clear that: [Initial only one.]

_____ I intend to include this treatment among the life-sustaining treatments that may be withheld or withdrawn.

_____ I do not intend to include this treatment among the life-sustaining treatments that may be withheld or withdrawn.

[If you do not agree with any of the printed directives and want to write your own, or if you want to write directives in addition to the printed provisions, or if you want to express some of your thoughts, you can do so here.]

_____

_____

_____	_____
Date	Your Signature
_____	_____
Your Address	Type or Print Your Name
_____	

The declarant voluntarily signed this document in my presence:

Witness _____

Address _____

_____

Witness _____

Address _____

_____

NOTARIZATION

On this the _____ day of _____ , _____ , the declarant, _____ , personally appeared before the undersigned officer and signed the foregoing instrument in my presence.

_____

Notary Public

[Seal]

My commission expires: _____

Exhibit 10–2 Sample Durable Power of Attorney for Health Care (Broad Form)

This is a sample of a durable power of attorney for health care provided for informational purposes only.

State of _____

County of_____

Know all persons by these presents, that I _____(Principal)_____ , of _____(Address)_____ , the undersigned, do hereby make and constitute and appoint _____(Name of Attorney in Fact)_____ , _____(State Relationship)_____ , of _____(Address)_____ , _____(City)_____ , _____(County)_____ , _____(State)_____ , as my true and lawful attorney in fact for me and in my name, place, and stead, giving unto said _____(Attorney in Fact)_____ full power and authority to perform all and every act and thing that I may legally do including, but not limited to, the power to reject or withdraw consent for medical procedures and treatment and to withhold or withdraw artificial nutrition or hydration, pursuant to state law, and every power necessary to carry out the purposes for which the power is granted, without full power of substitution and revocation, hereby ratifying and affirming that which my agent or attorney in fact shall lawfully do or cause to be done by him or her by virtue of the power herein conferred upon him or her.

In the event that my agent, _____(Name)_____ , shall fail to act for any reason, I hereby appoint _____(Alternative Attorney in Fact or Agent)_____ , (Address)_____ , _____(City)_____ , _____(County)_____ , _____(State)_____ , _____(Phone)_____ , as my attorney in fact or agent to all the powers above set forth.

This power of attorney shall not be affected by my disability or incapacity, or by uncertainty as to whether I am dead or alive, and it must be accepted and relied upon by anyone to whom it is presented until such person (1) receives written notice of revocation by me as guardian of my estate or by my appointed attorney in fact or (2) has actual knowledge of my death.

In witness whereof, I have signed this Durable Power of Attorney at the _____(City)_____ , _____(County)_____ , _____(State)_____ , this _____ day of _____ , _____ .

Signature   _____(Name of Principal)_____

Name   _____(Printed or Typed)_____

continues

Exhibit 10–2 continued

Witnesses:

Signature _____ Date _____

Printed Name _____ Phone _____

Residence Address _____

_____

Signature _____ Date _____

Printed Name _____ Phone _____

Residence Address _____

_____

NOTARIZATION

Subscribed and sworn to before me this _____ day of _____ ,

_____

_____ (Notary Public) _____

[Seal]

My commission expires _____

Exhibit 10–3 Sample Durable Power of Attorney for Health Care (Detailed Form)

This sample of a durable power of attorney for health care is provided for informational purposes only. Portions of this form are adapted from the American Bar Association Committee on Legal Problems for the Elderly.

Know all persons by these presents, that I, _____(Principal)_____ , of _____(Address)_____ , the undersigned, do hereby make and constitute and appoint _____(Name of Attorney in Fact or Agent)_____ , my _____ _____(Relationship)_____ , of ____(Address)____ , ____(City)____ , ____(County)____ , ____(State)____ , as my true and lawful attorney in fact for me and in my name, place, and stead, giving unto said _____ (Attorney in Fact)_____ full power and authority to:

1. Obtain and to have access to medical or health records or other medical information to the same extent I am entitled to it.
2. To hire, fire, or otherwise employ paramedical and supportive health care responsible for my care.
3. To enter into contracts of every nature with health care providers without my attorney in fact being held personally liable financially for said contracts.
4. To authorize or refuse to authorize any medications to alleviate pain, even though such medication may lead to addiction or physical damage or indirectly hasten my death, as long as there is no intentional act of any nature to cause my death because of said medication.
5. To consent or refuse to consent for any and all types of medical care, treatment, or procedures and the use of mechanical or other procedures affecting bodily function.
6. To authorize my admission or discharge to or from any health care facility, inpatient or outpatient (even if against medical advice).
7. To take any legal action to implement the directives herein at the expense of my estate.
8. To make anatomical gifts of part or all of my body for medical purposes.

As to LIFE-SUSTAINING TREATMENT: [Please initial one only.]

_____ AUTHORITY DISCRETIONARY WITH MY AGENT—I direct that my life not be prolonged and that no life-sustaining treatment be provided if my agent believes the burden outweighs the benefits of treatment. My agent shall consider the following in making a decision relating to life-sustaining treatment: the suffering or relief of suffering, the quality of life I have been accustomed to, and the total costs and expenses involved.

continues

Exhibit 10–3 continued

_____ DIRECTIVE TO WITHDRAW OR WITHHOLD TREAT-MENT—I do not want life-sustaining treatment if my agent and my attending physician believe I will be permanently unconscious or in a coma and are satisfied that this condition is incurable or irreversible and there is no or little likelihood of returning to me the ability to think or act for myself.

_____ MAXIMUM TREATMENT—I direct my agent to preserve my life as long as possible and without regard to my condition or my chances for recovery or cost.

_____ MY OWN DIRECTIVE— _____

_____

_____

Regarding HYDRATION AND NUTRITION provided to me by means of a nasogastric tube and tubes inserted into my stomach, intestines, or veins, I wish to make clear that: [Initial only one.]

_____ I intend to include this treatment among the life-sustaining treatments that may be withheld or withdrawn.

_____ I do not intend to include this treatment among the life-sustaining treatments that may be withdrawn or withheld.

In the event that my agent shall fail to act on my behalf for any reason, I hereby appoint _____(Name)_____ , _____(Address)_____ , _____(City)_____ , _____(County)_____ , _____(State)_____ , _____(Phone)_____ , my alternative attorney in fact or agent with all the powers above set forth.

It is the intent of this document to create a durable power of attorney for health care effective upon any period of incapacity in which, in the opinion of my attending physician and my attorney in fact or agent, I am unable to make or communicate a choice regarding a particular health care decision. This power of attorney shall not be affected by my disability or incapacity or by uncertainty as to whether I am dead or alive and it may be accepted as relied upon by anyone to whom it is presented until such person (1) receives written notice of revocation by me as the guardian of my estate or by my appointed attorney in fact or agent, or (2) has actual knowledge of my death.

continues

Exhibit 10–3 continued

I have discussed fully with my attorney in fact or agent my desires and wishes regarding the many health care decisions he or she may be required to make on my behalf. I am fully aware of the uncertainty of what may happen to me in the future as well as the variety of medical decisions that may need to be made for me. Therefore, I grant to my attorney in fact or agent full authority to make decisions for me regarding health care. In exercising this authority, my agent shall follow my wishes as stated in this document or otherwise known to my agent to be in my best interest.

My agent's authority to interpret my decisions is intended to be as broad as possible except for specific limitations as contained herein.

If, for any reason, a guardian over my person should be appointed by a court of competent jurisdiction, I nominate my agent or his or her successor named in this instrument to be such a guardian.

I do not hold any person who relies in good faith upon any representations made by my attorney in fact or agent, herein, to be liable to me, my estate, assignees, or heirs. The authority delegated under this durable power of attorney for health care is separable so that in the event one or more paragraphs are invalid, it shall not affect any other paragraph or authority as outlined herein.

In witness whereof, I have signed this Durable Power of Attorney for Health Care, on this _____ day of _____ , _____ .

Signature   ____(Name of Principal)____

Name   ____(Printed or Typed)____

Witnesses:

Signature _____ Date _____

Printed Name_____ Phone _____

Residence Address _____

_____

Signature _____ Date _____

Printed Name_____ Phone _____

Residence Address _____

continues

Exhibit 10–3 continued

NOTARIZATION

State of _____

County of_____

On this _____ day of _____ , _____ , the said _____ , known to me or satisfactorily proven to be the person named in the foregoing instrument, personally appeared before me, a Notary Public, written in and for the state and county aforesaid, and acknowledged that he or she freely and voluntarily executed the same for the purposes stated therein.

_____(Notary Public)_____

[Seal]

My commission expires _____

Exhibit 10–4 Sample General Durable Power of Attorney Including Health Care Decisions

---

Article I—Declarations

This durable power shall take effect upon its execution unless some other date is specified.

I, ___(Principal)___ , currently living at ___(Address)___ , appoint ___(Name of attorney in fact)___ as my attorney in fact with full power to carry out those acts specified in Article II in accordance with any limitations imposed herein. This power of attorney shall not be affected by my subsequent disability or incapacity.

This durable power of attorney shall become effective upon my incapacity to carry on my affairs as determined upon certification that such is the case by two physicians (one of whom shall be a forensic psychiatrist skilled in competency determinations), a geriatric assessment team composed of a psychiatrist, neurologist, psychologist, and social worker, at a minimum, or as otherwise specified.

Article II—Powers Granted

The following powers are granted to my attorney in fact to be used for my benefit and on my behalf in accordance with the direction specified herein.

As to any assets, real or personal, standing in my name, being held for my benefit or acquired for my benefit, I confer the following powers upon my attorney in fact:

1. As to any commercial, checking, saving, savings and loan, money market, treasury bills, mutual fund accounts, safe deposit boxes in my name or opened for my benefit—to open, withdraw, deposit into, close and to negotiate, endorse, or transfer any instrument affecting those accounts.
2. As to any promissory note receivable, secured or unsecured, or any accounts receivable—to collect on, compromise, endorse, borrow against, hypothecate, release, and reconvey that note and any related deed of trust.
3. As to any shares of stock, bonds, or any documents or instruments defined as securities under law—to open accounts with stockbrokers (on cash or margin), buy, sell, endorse, transfer, hypothecate, and borrow against.
4. As to any real property—to collect rents, disburse funds, keep in repair, hire professional property managers, lease to tenants, negotiate and

---

continues

Exhibit 10–4 continued

renegotiate leases, borrow against, renew any loan, sign any documents required for any such transaction, and to sell, subject to confirmation of court, any of the real property.

5. To hire and pay from my funds for counsel and service of professional advisors, physicians, dentists, accountants, attorneys, and investment counselors.

6. As to my income taxes and other taxes—to sign my name, hire preparers and advisors and pay for their services from my funds, and to do whatever is necessary to protect my assets from assessments as though I did those acts myself.

7. To apply for government and insurance benefits, to prosecute and to defend legal actions, to arrange for transportation and travel, and to partition community property to create separate property for me.

8. To sign and deliver a valid disclaimer under the Internal Revenue Code and the Probate Code, when, in your judgment, my own and my heirs' best interests would be served; to that end, to hire and to pay for legal and financial counsel to make that decision as to whether to file disclaimer.

9. To manage tangible personal property, including but not limited to moving, storing, selling, donating, or otherwise disposing of said property.

10. To make gifts to my children and grandchildren conforming to gift patterns made in earlier years, provided that due care is given to my future needs in the event of incapacity or disability.

11. To create one or more trusts for my benefit and to contribute to such trusts and receive income and/or principal from such trusts in accordance with their terms.

12. To claim an elective share of the estate of my deceased spouse.

13. To renounce fiduciary positions.

As to decisions related to my health care, I hereby grant the following powers to my attorney in fact within the limitations specified below:

1. To authorize or withhold authorization for medical and surgical procedures.

2. To authorize my admission to a medical, nursing, residential, or similar facility, and to enter into agreements for my care.

3. To arrange for my discharge, transfer from, or change in type of care provided.

continues

Exhibit 10–4 continued

4. To arrange and pay for consultation, diagnosis, or assessment as may be required for my proper care and treatment.
5. To authorize participation in medical, nursing, and social research consistent with my decision indicated below as to life-sustaining treatment and such ethical guidelines as may appropriately govern such research.
6. To authorize the transfer of such of my organs or parts of my body as I might have done under the Uniform Anatomical Gift Act, subject only to the limitations noted below.

I have initialed below paragraph [one, two, three, or four], which reflects my instruction to my attorney in fact with respect to decisions to withhold or withdraw life-sustaining treatment. Further, I direct my attorney in fact to convey this instruction to any physicians, nurses, caregiving organizations (including but not limited to hospitals, nursing homes, mental institutions, boarding facilities), and others that may carry some responsibility for my care:

1. I desire that my life be prolonged to the greatest extent possible, without regard to my condition, the chances I have for recovery or long-term survival, or the cost of the procedures. (_____)
2. If I am in a coma that my doctors have reasonably concluded is irreversible, I desire that life-sustaining or -prolonging treatments *not* be used. (_____)
3. If I have an incurable or terminal condition or illness and no reasonable hope of long-term recovery or survival, I desire that life-sustaining or -prolonging treatments *not* be used. (_____)
4. I do not desire treatment to be provided and/or continued if the burdens of the treatment outweigh the expected benefits. My attorney in fact is to consider the relief of suffering, the preservation or restoration of functioning, and the quality as well as the extent of the possible extension of my life. (_____)

Article III—Nomination of Guardian

If, after execution of the durable power of attorney, incompetency proceedings are initiated either for my estate or my person, I hereby nominate as my guardian for consideration by the court _____ (Name) _____ , residing at _____ (Address) _____ .

continues

Exhibit 10–4 continued

Article IV—Time Limitation

In the event that I have not become incompetent or incapacitated within seven (7) years* from the date of execution of this durable power of attorney, this power of attorney shall expire automatically without any further action by me. If, however, it has been utilized during any period prior to the expiration of that seven (7)-year period, it shall continue to be in effect for the duration of my incompetency or incapability and for seven (7) years thereafter.

I hereby sign my name to this Durable Power of Attorney this _____ day of _____ , _____ .

Witness: _____(Name)_____   _____(Date)_____

    _____

    _____(Name)_____   _____(Date)_____

    _____

*Any time period may be utilized.

CHAPTER 11

Legal Aspects of Medical Records

The purpose of the medical (clinical) health record is to provide complete information about each resident in the nursing facility, primarily for the use of facility personnel giving direct care and the attending physician. The maintenance of adequate and accurate health records in a current and complete form is required by state and federal statute and voluntary accrediting agencies; these requirements are promulgated, usually, under the rules and regulations of the state department of health. The nursing facility (or administrator, in some states) is responsible for the maintenance of health records. If a facility does not employ a full- or part-time medical records librarian, an employee of the facility must be assigned the responsibility of ensuring that records are maintained, completed, and returned. The person designated to keep the records must be professionally trained or trained by a professional medical records librarian and receive regular consultation from a person skilled in record maintenance.

Generally, the regulations require an accurate, well-maintained, and current system where medical records are readily accessible. A separate care record is kept for each resident individually in some type of folder, notebook, or chart holder in accordance with accepted professional standards and state laws and regulations. Each record is a chronological health and care history of the resident's stay, with every entry dated and signed by the caregiver. These records are kept up to date and complete, reflecting all information and the condition of each resident from the time of admission until discharge or death. All records are legibly written or printed in ink.

THE MEDICAL RECORD

As a general rule, the medical record consists of three sections: the personal or informational section, the medical or clinical section, and the nurses' section.

The **personal or informational section** is usually gathered at the time of admission to the nursing facility. It contains important statistical information about the resident, much of which is required by state regulation. This section, also known as the admission and discharge section, contains such items as:

- date of admission
- name and address
- age and sex
- marital status
- religion
- name, address, and telephone number of attending physician and alternate
- residents' rights and responsibilities form
- name and address of next of kin
- date and time of discharge or death
- resident transfer or outgoing referral
- discharge instructions, if returning home
- mortician's receipt and physician's orders to release body
- signed consents and release-of-information forms (here or in the medical section)

The **medical or clinical section** contains information relative to the medical or clinical aspects of the resident. Records normally included are:

- history and physical examination—prior to admission
  - medical history, family history, past illness of importance
  - positive physical findings
  - working diagnosis
  - physician's orders for medication, treatment, care, and diet
  - date and signature of examining physician
- physician's orders

- date of visit
- records of examinations and progress notes
- medication, treatment, care, and diet orders
- orders for restraints
- orders for extent of activity
- signature of examining physician
- X-ray, laboratory, and other medical reports
- consultation reports
- rehabilitation, physical therapy, occupational therapy, and social service reports
- final diagnosis

The **nurses' section** usually consists of reports and observations of the resident made by the nurse, including:

- date, time, quantity of dosage, method of administration of all medications, and signature of nurse administering them
- temperature, pulse, respiration, and blood pressure taken and recorded as specified by the attending physician's orders
- date and time of all treatments or dressings
- date and time of physician's and dentist's visits
- complete record of all restraints, including time, type, reason, and authority for applying restraints to residents
- record of all pertinent factors pertaining to the resident's condition
- record of any accident occurring while the resident is in the facility
- condition on discharge or transfer
- signature of nurse or aide

It is the duty of the nursing facility administrator to supply basic information at the time of any resident's transfer to another nursing facility or to a hospital.

Retention of the Medical Record

Usually, upon the death or discharge of a resident, the medical record is completed, bound, and retained in an inactive file for a period of years prescribed by state or federal law. The basis for retention of the record is determined by the nursing facility and prevailing medical practice in the absence of statutes, rules, and regulations in the particular state or applicable federal law. By rule of thumb, medical records are kept as long as there is an administrative need for them. Some say the primary consideration should be related to the statute of limitations in the particular state. State law requirements concerning the retention of medical records after discharge vary from five to seven years; the requirements under the Code of Federal Regulations are for five years, or three years after a resident reaches the state legal age.

CONFIDENTIALITY AND RELEASE OF INFORMATION

A number of states and the federal government treat the health record as a confidential document. The Department of Health and Human Services (HHS), in the Code of Federal Regulations, 42 CFR, Part 483.10(3e), October 1998, states, "The resident has the right to personal privacy and confidentiality of his or her personal and clinical records."

Generally, the ownership of the medical record determines who has the right to release or disclose the information and under what conditions. Some state statutes and regulations have declared that the medical record is owned by the nursing facility and have passed laws controlling this record and the information therein. However, Missouri regulations state, "No record or excerpts from any record shall be released from the record except upon the order of the patient or by due process of law. Records may be removed from the record room only upon the order of the administrator or by duly qualified persons for purposes of study and research."

It is largely agreed that the health record is the physical property of the facility. It is a peculiar type of property—the sheets of paper, etc., are the property of the facility but the content of the medical record is the property of the resident (or his or her next of kin, in some circumstances). Therefore, the resident or next of kin has the right to choose when to release or not release information from his or her record in absence of a court order. To disclose information from a resident's health record, the facility must have the consent of the resident or next of kin.

In certain situations, information may be disclosed by the facility without the consent of the resident. Such situations occur when an agency or individual has an ascertainable legal interest in the record, as determined by the court or nature of the agency. Although some courts have said that the attending physician has a legal interest in the health record, this does not give him or her the legal right to prevent disclosure of the information therein by the nursing facility.

Release of Information to the Court

If a court, by subpoena duces tecum or other duly authorized order, directs that a record be disclosed, the nursing facility must release the information or be held in contempt of court. Court orders for records are quite common in lawsuits involving personal injury, malpractice, insurance, workers' compensation, wills, and crime.

Release of Information to Governmental Agencies

If a nursing facility participates in Medicare or Medicaid, it is generally agreed that those agencies concerned with the administration of Medicare and Medicaid have an ascertainable legal interest in the health record. Thus, information may be disclosed to:

- the resident or his or her authorized representative
- the resident's attending physician or to the facility where the resident is receiving care, if there is consent by the resident, by his or her representative, or by a physician employed by HHS
- persons who have a demonstrable concern in protecting the interests of the resident (friend, employer, social agency, etc.), but only if good cause is shown

Very often, nursing facilities receive inquiries about information from the health record from veteran's hospitals, welfare organizations, health organizations, etc. The best procedure to follow regarding these requests is to obtain the resident's consent. If consent is refused, the agency must obtain a court order.

Release of Information to Insurance Companies

With the growth of third-party payers (Blue Cross and other commercial insurance companies), information concerning the resident is requested regularly by the insurance companies to determine whether or not payment of claims should be made. The courts recognize that these companies have an ascertainable legal interest in the health record on the basis that when a resident subscribes to an insurance program, there is at least an implied (in the absence of express release of such information to the company) consent that the resident intends to release information so that his or her claims can be processed. However, to be better protected, the usual practice is to obtain an executed release of information (to insurance companies) from all residents admitted to the facility.

Release of Information for Research and Education

If the medical information is used for research and study, the general rule is that no consent is required by the resident as long as his or her identity is fully protected. This is usually accomplished by providing a code system for identifying the medical records.

POLICIES FOR MEDICAL RECORDS

Guidelines for writing policies regarding the release of information from the medical record are as follows:

- The health record is kept for the benefit of the resident, physician, nursing facility staff, and medical research and education.
- Health records are not taken out of the nursing facility except upon a duly authorized order of the court.
- The nursing facility may use the health record, if necessary, to defend itself or its agents in a lawsuit.
- No information of a privileged or confidential nature is released from the health record without the proper authorization of the resident or, in absence of said release, without a duly executed order from a court. Physicians (other than the attending physician) must have proper authorization from the resident before information is released.
- All professional personnel working directly with the care of the resident have access to his or her health record. However, the release

of such information to a social service or other health agency must be obtained from the resident or his or her legal representative.

- Requests by the residents for medical information concerning their own conditions should be referred to the attending physician. If the resident insists upon obtaining the information, have him or her get a court order.
- If possible, medical records should not be removed from the area where the health records are filed or from the nursing station.
- If professional personnel wish to use a health record for research or education, they must obtain the consent of administration before doing so.
- Any employee releasing confidential information from a health record without the consent of the resident involved or the administration is subject to dismissal.

CHAPTER 12

Residents'
Bill of Rights

The Department of Health and Human Services (HHS), Health Care Financing Administration (HCFA), under the Omnibus Budget Reconciliation Act (OBRA) 1987, published the current Medicare and Medicaid requirements for long-term care facilities in the **Code of Federal Regulations**, 42 CFR, Part 430 to end, 10-1-98. These rules include the Residents' Bill of Rights. These rights are guaranteed to all residents in nursing facilities under state and federal law. Remedies for violations are provided to the resident to proceed against the facility according to these laws.

HHS and nursing facilities believe that the Residents' Bill of Rights contributes to more effective resident care in long-term care facilities. The Bill of Rights recognizes that the physician and the facility owe certain responsibilities to the resident. The following textual materials contain the actual federal rules and regulations pertaining to residents' rights and interpretations thereof. Some are interpretations by the author; others are verbatim from the Interpretive Guidelines. The Interpretive Guidelines do not have the effect of law but are opinions of experts in the field of long-term care administration. If there is a disagreement with an interpretation, it may be litigated in a state or federal court of law, and the judgment of the court has the effect of a final interpretation. Actual rules and regulations are in boldface type; interpretations are not.

The fact that a resident has been adjudicated incompetent, is medically incapable of understanding, or exhibits a communication barrier does not absolve the facility from advising the resident of his or her rights to the extent that the resident is able to understand them in part or when he or she recovers sufficiently to understand them. In a case where the resident is incapable of understanding his or her rights, the facility must so advise the guardian, next of kin, or sponsor.

To implement the residents' rights program, the staff social worker and activity director arrange a meeting of all residents physically and mentally able to understand the provisions of these rights. The Bill of Rights is read to the group and discussed. Each resident is provided with a copy and signs a dated statement that he or she has received this copy and that the contents have been read and explained to his or her satisfaction.

The administrator ensures that adequate inservice sessions are scheduled for the staff to familiarize them with the contents of the residents' rights policies expected to be implemented in the facility.

RESIDENTS' BILL OF RIGHTS
42 CFR, SEC 483.10, CH. IV (10-1-98)

Privacy and Respect

The resident has a right to a dignified existence, self-determination, and communication with and access to persons and services inside and outside the facility. A facility must protect and promote the rights of each resident.

Under this requirement, the **resident has a right** to:

1. **Personal privacy and confidentiality of his/her personal and clinical records.**

   Personal privacy includes accommodations, medical treatment, written and telephone communications, personal care, visits, and meetings of family and resident groups. This does not mean that the facility must provide a private room for each resident.

   Personal and clinical records include *all* types of records the facility might keep on a resident; they may be social, medical, financial, automated, or other records. The resident has the right to keep the record and the information in these records private. A violation of this right may result in a law action in invasion of privacy against the facility.

2. **Approve or refuse release of personal and clinical records to any individual outside the facility.**

A resident may refuse to release any information in any of the records the facility keeps on him or her.

The resident's right to refuse release of personal and clinical records does not apply when the resident is transferred to another health care institution or when record release is required by law.

3. **Reside and receive services in the facility with reasonable accommodation of individual needs and preferences except when the health and safety of the individual or other residents would be endangered.**

"Reasonable accommodation of individual needs and preferences" means that the facility can adapt certain physical areas and staff behavior to help the resident to have independent functioning, dignity, and well-being. It does not mean that there must be interior design modifications to a resident's room such as repainting walls and replacing carpeting or tile. Space may be created flexibly for various resident needs. For example, privacy for visitation or meetings may be arranged by using a dining area between meals, a vacant room, an office, or a chapel.

Covered also in the term *reasonable accommodation of needs* is the way the facility's physical environment is used to aid residents to maintain unassisted functioning. This includes making it easier for the resident to move about, the use of furniture and equipment that gives proper support for residents to stand by themselves without assistance (arm supports, correct chair heights, etc.), and the use of proper equipment for disabled residents in going to the bathroom (grab bars, elevated toilet seats, etc.). The facility must also have in place measures to make it safe for confused residents who wander, allowing them to walk around unrestrained. The facility should have readable calendars and clocks displayed, wall hangings reflecting the lives of residents, and other measures to encourage resident or resident-staff interaction.

4. **Receive notice before the resident's room or roommate in the facility is changed.**

The issue of notice regarding change of room or roommate is more fully explained under the section concerning transfer or discharge of the resident.

It is important, under this right, that the resident is informed in *advance* about a change in room or roommate and *why* the change is taking place. Another area of concern is whether or not the resident is moved when he or she asks to be moved.

5. **Refuse transfer to another room within the institution, if the purpose of the transfer is to relocate from the distinct part of the institution that is a skilled nursing facility (SNF) to a part of the institution that is not a SNF, or from a NF to a distinct part of the institution that is a SNF. The resident's exercise of this right does not affect his/her eligibility or entitlement to Medicaid benefits.**

6. **Exercise his/her right as a resident of the facility and as a citizen or resident of the United States.**

   "Exercising rights" means that the residents have autonomy and choice to the maximum extent possible about how they want to live their everyday lives and to receive care *subject* to the facility's rules affecting *resident conduct* and those regulations governing the protection of resident health and safety.

   In determining the rights of residents, there is always the weighing of the resident's rights against those of society. If society or other residents in the facility may be harmed, the resident may stand to lose some of his or her rights.

Under this requirement, the **facility must**:

1. **Care for its residents in a manner and in an environment that promotes maintenance or enhancement of each resident's quality of life.**

2. **Promote care for residents in a manner and in an environment that maintains or enhances each resident's dignity and respect in full recognition of his/her individuality.**

   "Dignity" means that the staff of the facility, in their work with residents, show an appreciation for and make every attempt to promote each resident's self-worth. Areas in which the staff can enhance the resident's self-image and self-worth relate to grooming, helping to dress, and respecting each resident's right to private space and property (for example, not changing the radio or television station without the resident's permission). The staff should also respect each resident's social status by speaking respectfully, listening carefully, and addressing each resident in the way he or she wishes.

3. **Inform the resident both orally and in writing in a language that the resident understands of his/her rights and of all rules and regulations governing resident conduct and responsibilities during the stay in the facility. Such notification must be made prior to or upon admission and during the resident's stay. Receipt of such information and any amendments to it must be acknowledged in writing.**

   "To inform the resident in a language that he or she understands" means that the passing on of information concerning rights and responsibilities must be both clear and understandable to the resident. If the resident cannot understand English, the rights must be explained in a language familiar to the resident.

   If languages other than English are commonly used in a local area, the facility must have written translations of its statement of rights and responsibilities and should make available the services of an interpreter in those languages.

   In the case of a language not common in a given local area, a representative of the resident may sign that he or she has interpreted the statement of rights to the resident prior to the resident's acknowledgment of receipt.

   For hearing-impaired residents who communicate by sign language, the facility is expected to provide an interpreter. Large-print texts of the facility statement of residents' rights and responsibilities should also be available.

   "Both orally and in writing" means that if a resident cannot read and understand written materials without assistance, an oral summary along with the written document is acceptable.

   "During the resident's stay" means that if the rules and regulations governing resident conduct or rights change, the facility must update residents about these changes.

   If a resident is adjudged incompetent under the laws of a State by a court of competent jurisdiction, the rights of the resident are exercised by the person appointed under State law to act on the resident's behalf.

   Any legal-surrogate designed in accordance with State law may exercise the resident's rights to the extent provided by State law where the resident has not been adjudged incompetent by the State court.

4. **Promptly notify the resident and (if known) the resident's legal representative or interested family member when there is a change in room or roommate assignment.**
5. **Promptly notify the resident and (if known) the resident's legal representative or interested family member when there is a change in resident's rights under Federal or State law or regulations.**
6. **Record and periodically update the address and phone number of the resident's legal representative or interested family member.**

Medical Care and Treatment

Under this requirement, the **resident has a right** to:

1. **Access all records pertaining to him/herself, including clinical records, within 24 hours of an oral or written request by the resident or his/her legal representative; and after receipt of his/ her records, to purchase at a cost (not to exceed the community standard) photocopies of the records or any portions of them upon request and 2 working days advance notice to the facility.**

    "Right to access" may apply either to the resident or to others based upon state law—for example, guardian, conservator, holder of durable power of attorney. It is important, when residents request to inspect their records, that there are no unnecessary delays in allowing them to do so.

    "Purchase" means that the resident may be charged for photocopy costs at the prevailing community charge. The information and content of the record is the resident's property, but the actual paper the record is written on is the property of the facility.

    "2 working days advance notice" means two business days, which excludes holidays and weekends.

    Should a resident wish to see his or her medical record contrary to the instructions of the attending physician, nursing staff should contact the physician, who may want to visit with the resident, family, or legal guardian before complying with the request.

2. **Be fully informed in language that he/she can fully understand of his/her total health status, including but not limited to his/her medical condition.**

"Total health status" includes medical care, nursing care, dietary needs, rehabilitation and restorative potential, activities, mental status, dental health status, psychosocial status, and sensory and physical impairments.

The resident should be consulted and involved in his or her assessment and care planning process, including a discussion, in language that the resident can understand, about his or her diagnosis, treatment choices, risks, if any, and prognosis.

3. **Refuse treatment and to refuse to participate in experimental research and to formulate an advance directive.**

When a resident refuses treatment, it is important that the refusal is documented in the resident's record. If possible, it is necessary to discuss with the resident the health and safety consequences of his or her refusal and any alternatives to the refused treatment. It is possible, if a resident refuses *all* treatment, that the only alternative for the facility is to discharge the resident on the grounds that the facility is incapable of meeting his or her health needs. This is explained further under transfer and discharge.

"Experimental research" means using residents to develop and test clinical treatments (new drugs or therapy) involving the treatment and control groups. If a resident is considered for participation in experimental research, he or she must be *fully* informed of the nature of the experiment and understand the possible consequences of participating. The resident or his or her legal representative must give *written* consent *prior* to participation. Experimental research must also respect the privacy of the resident; any direct observation requires the consent of the resident, his or her legal representative, or a family member. General resident statistics that do not identify individual residents may be used for studies without obtaining the resident's permission.

It is important that the facility have an institutional review board or other committee that reviews and approves research protocol.

See Chapter 10 for facility responsibilities in the area of advance directives.

4. **Choose a personal attending physician.**

The right to choose a personal physician does not mean that the physician must or will serve a resident, or that a resident must designate a personal physician.

If a resident does designate a personal physician and that physician fails to fulfill given requirements under Medicare/ Medicaid law, the facility *will* have the right, after informing the resident, to seek alternative physician participation to ensure the provision of appropriate and adequate care and treatment.

5. **Be fully informed in advance about care and treatment and of any changes in that care or treatment that may affect the resident's well-being.**

   "Informed in advance" means that the facility discusses with the resident or his or her legal representative treatment options and alternatives and that the resident selects and approves of the specific plan of care before it is instituted. This requirement does not apply to emergency procedures in life-threatening situations unless advance directions are in effect.

6. **Participate in planning care and treatment or changes in care and treatment unless adjudicated incompetent or otherwise found to be incapacitated under the laws of the State.**

7. **Self-administer drugs if the interdisciplinary team has determined that this practice is safe.**

   The interdisciplinary team includes the attending physician, a registered nurse with responsibility for the resident, and other appropriate staff depending upon the resident's needs and with participation of the resident or legal representative, to the extent practicable.

   The interdisciplinary team must ask the resident during his or her assessment whether he or she wishes to self-administer drugs. If the resident says no, the resident has exercised his or her right and the responsibility then becomes that of the facility. If the resident says yes, the interdisciplinary team must assess the resident's understanding and physical and visual ability to carry out this responsibility. If the interdisciplinary team determines that the resident is incapable of carrying out this responsibility because of a danger to the resident or others, the team may withdraw this right.

   It is the responsibility of the nursing staff to record self-administered doses in the resident's medication administration record.

   Medication errors occurring with residents who self-administer drugs should not be counted in the facility's medication error rate.

A number of medication errors by the resident should call into question the judgment made by the facility in allowing the resident to self-administer drugs.

Under this requirement, the **facility must**:

1. **Immediately inform the resident; consult with the resident's physician; and (if known) notify the resident's legal representative or interested family member when there is**
   a. **an accident involving the resident which results in injury and has the potential for requiring physician intervention;**
   b. **a significant change in the resident's physical, mental, or psychosocial status (i.e., a deterioration in health, mental, or psychosocial status in either life-threatening conditions or clinical complications);**
   c. **a need to alter treatment significantly (i.e., a need to discontinue an existing form of treatment due to adverse consequences, or to commence a new form of treatment);**
   d. **a decision to transfer or discharge the resident from the facility.**
2. **Inform each resident of the name, specialty, and way of contacting the physician responsible for his/her care.**
   If the facility has a clinic or similar arrangement, it should supply residents with the name and contact information for the primary physician and/or central number for the clinic staff.

Freedom from Abuse and Restraint

Under this requirement, the **resident has the right** to:

1. **Be free of interference, coercion, discrimination, or reprisal from the facility in exercising his/her rights.**
   The facility must not hamper, compel by force, treat differently, or retaliate against a resident for exercising his or her rights.
   The facility may and should support and encourage resident participation in meeting care-planning goals as documented in the resident assessment and care plan. This is not interference or coercion.

Examples of trying to limit the choice of the resident in exercising his or her rights are:

- reducing the group activity time of a resident trying to organize a resident group
- requiring residents to seek prior approval to distribute information about the facility
- discouraging a resident from hanging a religious ornament above his or her bed
- isolating residents for prejudicial treatment
- assigning inexperienced aides to a resident with long-term care needs because the resident exercises his or her rights

2. **Be free from any physical restraints imposed or psychoactive drug administered for the purposes of discipline or convenience and not required to treat the resident's medical symptoms.**

"Physical restraints" are any manual methods, physical or mechanical devices, or material or equipment *attached* or adjacent to the resident's body in a way that the individual cannot remove the restraint easily, and the restraint restrains freedom of movement or normal access to the body by the resident. Common examples of physical restraints are leg restraints, arm restraints, hand mittens, soft ties or vests, wheelchair safety bars, and geriatric chairs.

"Psychoactive drugs" are drugs prescribed to control mood, mental status, or behavior.

"Discipline" is any action taken by the facility for the purpose of punishing or penalizing residents.

"Convenience" is any action taken by the facility to control resident behavior or maintain residents with the least amount of effort by the facility and not in the best interest of the resident but for the benefit of the facility.

"Less restrictive measures" than restraints (pillows, pads, removable lap trays) are often effective in achieving proper body positions, balance, and alignment and in preventing contractions.

A facility *must* have *evidence* of consultation with health professionals (occupational or physical therapists) in the use of less restrictive support devices *prior to* using physical restraints.

If, after a *trial of less restrictive measures*, the facility decides that a physical restraint would enable and promote greater functional independence, the use of the restraining device must *first be explained* to the resident, family member, or legal representative. If the resident, family member, or legal representative agrees to this treatment alternative, the restraining device may be used for specific periods for which the restraint has been determined to help.

If there are life-threatening medical symptoms (dehydration, electrolyte imbalance, urinary blockage, etc.), a restraint may be used temporarily to provide necessary life-saving treatment. Physical restraints may be used for *brief periods* to allow medical treatment to proceed if there is *documented evidence* of the resident, family, or legal representative approval of the treatment.

One consideration in the use of restraints is staff consultation with the resident, family, or legal representative in weighing the risks and benefits of using physical restraints.

There should be some evidence in the resident's care plan that the *need for restraints is periodically reevaluated and that efforts to eliminate their use have been made.*

3. **Be free from verbal, sexual, physical and mental abuse, corporal punishment, and involuntary seclusion.**

Residents are not to be abused by anyone. This includes facility staff, other residents, consultants, volunteers, staff of other agencies serving the resident, family members, legal guardians, friends, and other individuals.

"Verbal abuse" means any use of oral, written, or gestured language, including disparaging and derogatory terms in relation to residents or their families. Also prohibited is describing residents in a derogatory way within their hearing regardless of their age, ability to comprehend, or disability.

"Sexual abuse" includes sexual harassment, coercion, and assault.

"Physical abuse" includes hitting, slapping, punching, kicking, and controlling behavior of the resident through corporal punishment.

"Involuntary seclusion" means separation of a resident from other residents or from his or her room against the resident's will or the will of the resident's legal representative.

"Temporary monitored separation" from other residents is not considered involuntary seclusion if used as therapeutic intervention to reduce agitation as determined by *professional staff* and consistent with the resident's plan of care.

"Mental abuse" includes humiliation, harassment, threats of punishment, and deprivation.

Under this requirement, the **facility must**:

1. **Develop and implement written policies and procedures that prohibit mistreatment, neglect, and abuse of residents and misappropriation of resident's property.**

   As part of the written policies and procedures developed by the facility under this section, there should be a mechanism for the investigation of alleged violations of abuse or neglect. Any alleged violations of individual rights are thoroughly investigated and appropriate action taken and documented.

2. **Not use verbal, mental, sexual, or physical abuse, including corporal punishment or involuntary seclusion.**

3. **Not employ individuals who have been found guilty of abusing, neglecting, or mistreating individuals by a court of law.**

4. **Have a finding entered into the State nurse aide registry concerning abuse, neglect, mistreatment of residents, or misappropriation of their property.**

5. **Report any knowledge of actions by a court of law against an employee that would indicate unfitness for services as a nurse aide or other NF staff to the State nurse aide registry or licensing authorities.**

6. **Ensure that all alleged violations involving mistreatment, neglect, or abuse (including injuries of an unknown source) and misappropriation of a resident's property are reported immediately to the administrator of the facility and other officials in accordance with State law through established procedures.**

7. **Must have evidence that all alleged violations are thoroughly investigated and must prevent further potential abuse while the investigation is in progress.**

8. **Must report the results of all investigations to the administrator or his/her designated representative and other officials in accordance with State law within 5 working days of the incident; and, if the alleged violation is verified, appropriate corrective action must be taken.**

Freedom of Association and Communication in Privacy

Under this requirement, the **resident has the right** to:

1. **Examine the results of the most recent survey of the facility conducted by Federal or State surveyors and any plan of correction in effect with respect to the facility.**

    "Survey results" means the Statement of Deficiencies and Plan of Correction, if required.

    The posting of the results of a survey "in a place readily available to the residents" means at eye level in a central **public place** in the facility, such as a lobby or in areas frequently visited by most residents.

2. **Receive information from agencies acting as client advocates and be afforded the opportunity to contact these agencies.**

3. **Privacy in written communications, including the right to send and receive mail promptly that is unopened, and have access to stationery, postage, and writing implements at the resident's own expense.**

    "Promptly," as used in this section, means delivery to the resident within 24 hours of arrival in the facility and delivery to the Postal Service within 24 hours, except on weekends.

    Some of the things surveyors look for include:
    - Is the resident's mail sealed when he or she receives it?
    - Does the resident have access to stationery, paper, and writing materials?

4. **Receive visitors, and the facility must allow access to the resident for such visitors at any reasonable hour.**

    "At any reasonable hour" means at least eight hours per day arranged in such a way that daytime, evening, and weekend visitation times are available to meet most health practitioner and nonfamily visitor schedules. The resident retains the right to refuse to see a visitor.

5. **Immediate access by**
    a. **any representative of the Secretary of HHS;**
    b. **any representative of the State;**
    c. **the resident's individual physician;**
    d. **the State long-term care ombudsman;**

     e. the agency responsible for the protection and advocacy system for developmentally disabled individuals;

     f. the agency responsible for the protection and advocacy system for mentally ill individuals;

     g. immediate family or other relatives of the resident subject to the resident's right to deny or withdraw consent at any time;

     h. others who are visiting with the consent of the resident subject to reasonable restrictions and the resident's right to deny or withdraw consent at any time.

6. **Have reasonable access to the use of a telephone where calls can be made without being overheard.**

"Private" means hearing privacy and, to the extent feasible, visual privacy.

Surveyors look for telephone equipment that accommodates residents who are hearing impaired and wheelchair bound. They also inquire as to the means of residents to make private calls, whether the resident receives assistance when needed, and whether the resident receives his or her messages.

7. **Share a room with his or her spouse when married residents live in the same facility and both spouses consent to the arrangement.**

A request by both spouses to share a room must be honored even if case-mix and other classification groups vary.

Facilities are not required to grant room-sharing rights to nonmarried consenting adults.

The facility must explain its policies on room-sharing requests to prospective residents prior to admission.

Facilities should attempt to accommodate residents' wishes and preferences in roommates whenever possible.

8. **Participate in social, religious, and community activities that do not interfere with the rights of other residents in the facility.**

The facility should accommodate, if possible, an individual's needs and choices for how he or she spends time inside and outside the facility.

9. **Organize and participate in resident groups in the facility.**

This right does *not* mean that residents *must* organize a family group. However, whenever residents or their families want to organize, facilities *must* allow such organizations to exist. The facility is required to provide the group with space, privacy for meetings, and staff support. Normally, the designated staffperson responsible for assistance and liaison between the group and facility administration is the only staffperson present during resident or family group meetings—and only if the group requests assistance.

The resident's family has the right to meet in the facility with the families of other residents in the facility.

A *resident* or *family group* means a group that meets regularly to discuss and offer suggestions about facility policies and procedures affecting the residents' care, treatment, and quality of life; to plan resident and family activities; to participate in individual activities; and for any other purpose.

Under this requirement, the **facility must**:

1. **Post the results of the most recent survey in a place readily accessible to residents.**
2. **Provide reasonable access to any resident by any entity or individual that provides health, social, legal, or other services to the resident (subject to the resident's right to deny or withdraw consent at any time).**
3. **Allow representatives of the State ombudsman to examine a resident's clinical records with the permission of the resident or the resident's legal representative and consistent with the State law.**
4. **Provide a resident or family group (if one exists) with private space.**
5. **Provide a designated staff person responsible for providing assistance and responding to written requests that result from group meetings.**
6. **Listen to the views and act upon the grievances and recommendations of residents and families concerning proposed policy and operational decisions affecting resident care and life in the facility.**

Activities

Under this requirement, the **resident has the right** to:

1. Choose activities, schedules, and health care consistent with his or her interests, assessments, and plans of care.
2. Interact with members of the community both inside and outside the facility.
3. Make choices about aspects of his/her life in the facility that are significant to the resident.

Under this requirement, the **facility must**:

1. Provide medically related social services and ongoing programs of activities to attain or maintain the highest practicable physical, mental, or psychosocial well-being of each resident.
   The surveyor may inquire whether or not the resident can make free choices as to:
   a. Getting up or retiring in the evening,
   b. Eating of meals other than at scheduled mealtimes,
   c. Eating with residents of their choice,
   d. Leaving the facility for short periods of time,
   e. Planning of their own daily activities.

Work

Under this requirement, the **resident has the right** to:

1. Refuse to perform services for the facility.
2. Perform services for the facility if he/she chooses, when:
   a. The facility has documented the need or desire for work in the plan of care;
   b. The plan specifies the nature of the services performed and whether the services are voluntary or paid;
   c. Compensation paid for services is at or above prevailing rates; and
   d. The resident agrees to the work arrangement described in the plan of care.
   "Prevailing rate" means the wage paid to nondisabled workers in the community surrounding the facility for the same type, quality, and quantity of work requiring comparable skills.

All of a resident's work, whether voluntary or paid, *must* be part of his or her plan of care. A resident's desire to work is subject to medical consideration. If the work is a part of a resident's plan of care, the therapeutic assignment must be formally agreed to by the resident. The resident has the right to refuse such treatment at any time.

Personal Possessions

Under this requirement, the **resident has the right** to:

1. **Retain and use personal possessions, including some furnishings and appropriate clothing, as space permits unless to do so would infringe upon the rights or health and safety of other residents.**
   All of the resident's possessions, regardless of their value to others, must be treated with respect for what they are and for what they represent to the resident. This right assures the resident that his or her personal possessions are important. The right to retain and use them creates a homelike environment.
   The facility may be held liable for negligently handling the private possessions of residents. Therefore, the facility should make every reasonable effort to advise the resident of the risks of having valuable items in the facility. The facility should encourage labeling of all resident personal possessions kept in the facility. It is the facility's responsibility to investigate promptly incidence of loss or damage to property.
   Many of the property right disputes might be handled through the resident and family groups.

Grievances and Complaints

Under this requirement, the **resident has the right** to:

1. **Voice grievances without discrimination or reprisal. Such grievances include those with respect to treatment which has been furnished as well as that which has not been furnished; and**

2. **Prompt efforts by the facility to resolve grievances the resident may have, including those with respect to behavior of other residents.**

Under this requirement, the **facility must**:

1. **Furnish a written description of the legal rights which includes:**
   a. **The manner of protecting personal funds,**
   b. **The resident's right to file a complaint with the State survey and certification agency concerning resident abuse, neglect, and misappropriation of resident property in the facility.**

Financial Affairs

Under this requirement, the **resident has the right** to:

1. **Manage his/her financial affairs and the facility may not require residents to deposit their personal funds with the facility.**

   Unless the resident has been determined incompetent by a court under state law, the resident has a right to manage his or her own financial affairs and is under no moral or legal obligation to deposit personal funds with the facility. If the resident chooses, he or she may ask the facility to manage his or her funds and, in that case, the facility must manage the funds. The facility must keep the resident's funds in an account or accounts that are separate from facility operating funds and funds of any person other than another resident (pooled residents' funds are permitted).

   Whether the account is individual or pooled, the facility must maintain a system that ensures a full, complete, and separate accounting of each resident's assets and earnings. In the case of a pooled account, an individual resident's share of earnings must be protected regularly. The facility must afford the resident or legal representative reasonable access to the record.

Under this requirement, the **facility**:

1. **Must inform each resident who is entitled to Medicaid benefits in writing at the time of admission to the nursing facility or when the resident becomes eligible for Medicaid of:**

a. The items and services that are included in nursing facility services under the State plan and for which the resident may not be charged.

b. Those other items and services that the facility offers and for which the resident may be charged and the amount of charges for these services.

2. Must inform the resident before or at the time of admission and periodically during the resident's stay of services available in the facility and of the charges for those services, including any charges for services not covered under Medicare or by the facility's per diem rate.

"Periodically," in this section, means as often as the facility changes its services or the charges for these services.

If, upon admission or during the stay of a resident, a Medicare SNF provider believes that Medicare will not pay for skilled nursing or specialized rehabilitation services, the facility must inform the resident or his or her legal representative in writing why these specific services may not be covered. The provider must keep a copy of this letter on file.

If the resident requests that the bill be submitted for the intermediary or coverage carrier for a Medicare decision, evidence that this submission has occurred should appear in the resident's record.

Advance notice to the resident of changes in services or charges is not required. Whenever possible, however, advance notice should be given in order to be consistent with the intent of the law, which is to allow residents to be fully informed of what they owe the facility. The burden of proof is a good faith effort to inform the resident *fully* of services and charges and related changes.

3. Furnish a written description of legal rights which includes:

a. A description of the manner of protecting personal funds;

b. A description of the requirements and procedures for establishing eligibility for Medicaid, including the right to request assessment which determines the extent of a couple's non-exempt resources at the time of institutionalization and attributes to the community spouse an equitable share of resources which cannot be considered available toward the cost of the institutionalized spouse's medical care in his/her process of spending down to Medicaid eligibility levels;

    c. A posting of names, addresses, and telephone numbers of all pertinent State client advocacy groups, such as: the State survey and certification agency, State licensure office, State ombudsman program, the protection and advocacy network, and Medicaid fraud control unit; and

    d. A statement that the resident may file a complaint with the State survey and certification agency concerning resident abuse, neglect, and misappropriation of resident property.

4. Must display prominently in the facility written information and provide to residents and potential residents oral and written information about how to apply for and use Medicare and Medicaid benefits and how to receive funds for previous payments covered by such benefits.

5. Must, upon written authorization of a resident, hold, safeguard, manage, and account for the personal funds of the resident deposited with the facility and

    a. the facility must deposit any resident's personal funds in excess of $50.00 in an interest-bearing account (or accounts) that is separate from any of the facility's operating accounts and that credits all interest earned on the resident's account to his/her account;

    b. the facility must maintain a resident's personal funds that do not exceed $50.00 in a non-interest-bearing account or petty cash fund.

6. Must establish and maintain a system that assures a full, complete, and separate accounting, according to generally accepted accounting principles, of each resident's personal funds entrusted to the facility on the resident's behalf and

    a. the system must preclude any commingling of resident funds with facility funds or with the funds of any person other than another resident;

    b. the individual financial record must be available through quarterly statement on request to the resident or his/her legal representative.

7. Must notify each resident who receives Medicaid benefits

    a. when the amount in the resident's account reaches $200.00 less than the Social Security Insurance (SSI) resource limit for one person;

b. that if the amount in the account in addition to the value of the resident's other non-exempt resources reaches the SSI resource limit for one person, the resident may lose eligibility for Medicaid or SSI.

8. Must convey within 30 days the resident's funds and a final accounting of those funds to the individual or probate jurisdiction administering the resident's estate upon the death of a resident with a personal fund deposited with the facility.

9. Must purchase a surety bond, or otherwise provide assurance satisfactory to the Secretary, to assure the security of all personal funds of the residents deposited with the facility.

10. May not impose a charge against the personal funds of a resident for any item or service for which payment is made under Medicare or Medicaid (except for applicable deductible, copayments, and coinsurance amounts). The facility may charge the resident for requested services that are more expensive or in excess of covered services.

    a. During the course of a covered Medicare or Medicaid stay, the facility *may not* charge for the following categories of items and services: nursing services, dietary services, activities programs as required, and certain routine personal hygiene items and services required to meet the needs of residents.

    b. Following are general categories and examples of items and services that the facility *may* charge to the resident's funds if they are requested by the resident, the facility informs the resident that there will be a charge, and payment is not made by Medicare or Medicaid: telephone; personal comfort items and TV/radio, clothing, reading matter, flowers and plants; social events and entertainment outside activities program; noncovered special services (i.e., privately hired aides and nurses); private room (except if therapeutically required); specially prepared or alternative food requested.

11. Must not charge a resident for any item or service not requested by the resident.

    a. The facility must inform the resident requesting an item or service for which a charge will be made that there will be a charge and what the charge will be.

Admission, Transfer, and Discharge Rights

Admissions Policy

Under this requirement, the **facility:**

1. **Must not require a third-party guarantee of payment to the facility as a condition of admission, expedited admission, or continued stay in the facility.**
2. **Must not charge, solicit, accept, or receive in addition to any amount otherwise required to be paid under the State plan, any gift, money, donation, or other consideration as a precondition of admission, expedited admission, or continued stay in the facility in the case of a person eligible for Medicaid.**
3. **Must not require residents or potential residents to waive their rights to Medicare or Medicaid.**
4. **Must not require oral or written assurance that residents or potential residents are not eligible for, or will not apply for, Medicare or Medicaid benefits.**
5. **May require an individual who has legal access to a resident's income or resources available to pay for care to sign a contract (without incurring personal financial liability) to provide the facility payment liability from resident's income or resources.**
6. **Must not require a resident to request any item or service as a condition of admission or continued stay.**
7. **May charge a resident who is eligible for Medicaid for items and services the resident has requested and received and that are not specified in the State plan as included in the term "nursing facility services" so long as the facility gives proper notice of the availability and cost of these services to residents and does not condition the resident's admission or continued stay on the request for and receipt of such additional services.**
8. **May solicit, accept, or receive a charitable, religious, or philanthropic contribution from an organization or from a person unrelated to a Medicaid-eligible resident or potential resident, but only to the extent that the contribution is not a condition of admission, expedited admission, or continued stay in the facility for a Medicaid eligible resident.**

States or political subdivisions may apply stricter admissions standards under State or local laws than those mentioned above to prohibit discrimination against individuals entitled to Medicaid benefits.

Equal Access to Quality Care

Under this **requirement**:

1. **The facility must establish and maintain identical policies and practices regarding transfer, discharge, and the provision of services under the State plan for all individuals regardless of source of payment.**
2. **The facility may charge any amount for services furnished non-Medicaid residents consistent with the notice requirements and describing the charges.**
3. **The State is not required to offer additional services on behalf of a resident other than services provided in the State plan.**

Bed-Hold Policy

Under this requirement, the **facility must**:

1. **Provide written information to the resident and a family member or legal representative before transferring a resident to a hospital or allowing a resident to go on a therapeutic leave, that specifies**
   a. **the duration of the bed-hold policy under the State plan (if any) during which the resident is permitted to return and resume residence in the facility; and**
   b. **the facility's policies regarding bed-hold periods permitting a resident to return.**
2. **Provide written notice to the resident and a family member or legal representative at the time of transfer of a resident to a hospital or for therapeutic leave which specifies the duration of the State and facility bed-hold policies.**
3. **Must establish and follow a written policy under which a resident whose hospitalization or therapeutic leave exceeds the bed-hold period under the State plan is readmitted to the facility immedi-**

ately upon the first availability of a bed in a semiprivate room, if the resident

    a. requires the services provided by the facility, and

    b. is eligible for Medicaid nursing facility services.

Transfer and Discharge

Transfer and discharge includes the movement of a resident to a bed outside of the certified facility whether the bed is in the same physical plant or not. Transfer and discharge does not refer to movement of a resident to a bed within the same certified facility.

Under this requirement, the **facility must**:

1. **Permit each resident to remain in the facility and not transfer or discharge the resident from the facility unless**
   a. **the transfer or discharge is necessary for the resident's welfare and needs that cannot be met in the facility;**
   b. **the transfer or discharge is appropriate because the resident's health has improved sufficiently so the resident no longer needs the services provided by the facility;**
   c. **the safety of the individuals in the facility is endangered;**
   d. **the health of individuals in the facility would otherwise be endangered;**
   e. **the resident has failed after reasonable and appropriate notice to pay for (or to have paid under Medicare or Medicaid) a stay at the facility. (For a resident who becomes eligible for Medicaid after admission, the facility may charge the resident only allowable charges under Medicaid); or**
   f. **the facility ceases to operate.**

In each case, for transfer under (a) through (e), the basis for the transfer or discharge must be documented in the resident's clinical record by the resident's physician and the interdisciplinary care planning team.

The facility has the burden of demonstrating that appropriate remedial efforts have been made and have failed before discharging a resident because of his or her behavior.

The facility must provide the resident proper notification before moving him or her to a different room.

The relocation of a resident upon discharge should be a planned event. The facility staff should handle the transfer or discharge in a way that minimizes resident and family anxiety.

Sufficient preparation by the facility may include trial visits by the resident to a new location, working with the family in helping to ensure that personal possessions are not left or lost, orienting the facility staff to resident's daily patterns, and reviewing with the facility staff routines for handling transfers and discharges to minimize transfer trauma.

2. **See that the resident's clinical record is documented when the facility transfers or discharges a resident under any of the above circumstances, by**
   a. **the resident's physician when transfer or discharge is necessary to meet the resident's needs or she/he no longer needs the facility's services; and**
   b. **a physician when transfer or discharge is necessary where the health of individuals in the facility would be otherwise endangered.**
3. **Provide sufficient preparation and orientation to residents to ensure safe and orderly transfer or discharge from the facility.**
4. **Must before transfer or discharge**
   a. **notify the resident and (if known) a family member or legal representative of the resident of the transfer or discharge and the reasons for the move in writing and in a language and manner they can understand at least 30 days beforehand (except as noted below),**
   b. **record the reasons in the resident's clinical record, and**
   c. **include the items the resident has failed to pay for.**
5. **May make notice as soon as practicable before transfer or discharge when**
   a. **the safety of individuals in the facility would be endangered;**
   b. **the health of individuals in the facility would be endangered;**
   c. **the resident's health improves to allow a more immediate transfer;**
   d. **an immediate transfer or discharge is required by the resident's urgent medical needs;**
   e. **a resident has not resided in the facility for 30 days.**
6. **Must include the following in the content of the notice transfer or discharge:**

a. the reason for discharge or transfer,
b. the effective date of transfer or discharge,
c. the location to which the resident is transferred or discharged,
d. a statement that the resident has the right to appeal the action to the State,
e. the name, address, and telephone number of the State long-term care ombudsman,
f. for residents with developmental disabilities, the mailing address and telephone number of the agency responsible for the protection and advocacy of developmentally disabled individuals,
g. for mentally ill residents, the mailing address and telephone number of the agency responsible for the protection and advocacy of mentally ill individuals.

Glossary of Legal Terms

Abuse—Concerning resident abuse, refers to ill treatment by coarse, insulting words or harmful acts.

Advance directive—A written instrument (such as a living will or durable power of attorney for health care) given by a competent adult to his or her agent, to become operative in the event of incapacity or incompetency.

Affidavit—A written or printed declaration or statement of facts made voluntarily and confirmed by oath or affirmation of the party making it, usually before a notary public.

Agent—A person authorized by another to act for him or her.

Aggrieved—A person who has suffered a loss or injury.

Allegation—Declaration of what a plaintiff or defendant intends to prove.

Assault—An intentional tort threatening bodily injury and creating fear or apprehension in another.

Assignment—Transfer of rights of real or personal property to another person.

Attorney in fact—A party authorized by another to act in his or her place for some particular purpose.

Battery—An unlawful touching of another without his or her consent.

Cause of action—The fact or facts that give a person a right to judicial redress or relief against another.

Civil law—That law dealing with actions between private parties where a government subdivision is not a party.

Claimant—One who claims or asserts a right, demand, or claim.

Code of Federal Regulations (CFR)—A publication containing codified laws, rules, and regulations of federal agencies. Title 42 CFR Part 405 etc. concerns Medicare and Medicaid requirements for long-term care facilities.

Common law—That body of law that derives its authority from usages and decrees of the courts.

Competent—Legally fit and with a mental capacity to understand the nature of his or her acts.

Complainant—One who signs a complaint in a criminal lawsuit.

Contract—An agreement between two or more persons to which the law attaches a legal obligation.

Corporate negligence—A breach of duty owed to a person by a business entity.

Criminal charge—A charge concerning violation of a criminal statute.

Criminal law—That body of law where the parties to an action involve the violation of a criminal statute.

DNI—Do not inhalate.

DNR—Do not resuscitate.

Damages—A money compensation recovered in the courts by any person who has suffered loss or injury. *Liquidated damages* are the amount of damages as determined by a judgment or a specific sum of money agreed to by the parties. *Punitive damages* are those relating to the punishment of a defendant for a willful, malicious, or intentionally fraudulent act, or for outrageous conduct.

Decedent—One who has passed away. Used in law of wills and estates.

Declarant—A person who makes a declaration, such as an advance directive.

Deed—A written conveyance of title, duly notarized, from one person to another.

Defamation—Libel or slander; an untrue statement injuring the character or reputation of another among a respectable class of society.

Defendant—The person or entity against whom a legal action is brought in court.

Defense—The facts a defendant must prove to justify his or her actions so that the plaintiff may not recover.

Deposition—Testimony of a witness under oath; for use in legal proceedings.

Durable power of attorney—A written instrument authorizing another to act as agent on his or her behalf. The instrument becomes effective when the principal becomes disabled.

Durable power of attorney for health care—A legal document where the principal appoints an agent to make all types of health care decisions if and when the principal becomes incapable of making them. A health care proxy is used in states where there are no laws covering durable power of attorney for health care.

Equity—Justice by what is fair in a particular situation, in contrast to strictly formulated common law.

Estate—All real or personal property in which one has an interest of ownership.

Executor—A male person appointed under a will to administer an estate of the decedent.

Executrix—A female person appointed under a will to administer an estate of the decendent.

Felony—A crime punishable by a prison term of one year or more.

Fiduciary—Acting in another's behalf with duties involving good faith, truth, confidence, honesty, and reasonable care.

Fraud—An intentional false representation to deceive another so that he or she shall act upon it to his legal injury.

Holographic will—A will that is handwritten, dated, and signed by the one making the will.

Implied—Where intention is not shown by specific words.

Incompetence—Lack of legal ability to understand the nature of one's act.

Independent contractor—One who is personally liable for his or her negligent acts.

Informed consent—An agreement allowing something to happen (medical treatments and procedures, surgery, etc.) based on full disclosure of facts, risks, alternatives, etc.

Injunction—An order issued by a court directing that a certain act be done or not done.

Intestate—Describes one who dies without a will.

Invasion of privacy—An intentional tort violating the right of privacy.

Jurisdiction—Power of a court to hear the facts of a case, apply the law, and declare judgment.

Law—A set of rules and principles established and enforced by a governing body.

Legacy—A disposition of personal property under a will.

Legal guardian—A person appointed by a court to handle the affairs of one who is incompetent.

Legal issue—Basic disputed point or question to which the parties of a lawsuit need a decision by a judge or jury.

Liable—Having the responsibility to compensate a legal wrong to another.

Libel—A written form of defamation.

Lien—An encumbrance upon personal or real property.

Litigation—Lawsuit; legal action.

Living will—A document that gives precise instructions directly to a physician, directing the life-sustaining treatment the signer is to receive or not receive in the event of a terminal illness or condition and inability to participate in medical decisions.

Malpractice—A negligent act by one who is a professional.

Misappropriation of property—Term used by the Omnibus Budget Reconciliation Act (OBRA) relative to the stealing of resident's personal property. There must be specific intent to steal, not the mere negligence of handling the property.

Misdemeanor—A lesser criminal act, usually punishable by one year or less in a county prison.

Negligence—Omitting to do an act that a reasonably prudent person would do under the same conditions and circumstances.

Negotiation—An act settling or arranging terms of a transaction.

Notary public—A public officer who administers oaths.

Personal representative—A person appointed by a testator to carry out the directions and requests in his or her will and to dispose of the property accordingly.

Plaintiff—One who brings an action at law in court.

Power of attorney—A written instrument authorizing another to act as one's agent.

Principal—In agency law, the person appointing an agent to act for him or her under certain circumstances.

Privileged communication—A confidential communication between physician and patient, husband and wife, lawyer and client, or clergy and penitent.

Probate law—Law that deals with wills and estates.

Public law—Law involving a government subdivision such as criminal, administrative, or constitutional law.

Ratification—Confirmation of a previous act done by a party or another.

Respondeat superior—A form of vicarious liability, meaning "Let the master respond for the acts of his or her agents."

Seizure—Forcibly taking possession of property.

Slander—A form of oral defamation.

Statute of limitations—The time period in which an action must be started.

Subpoena—An order from a court directing a person to appear before the court in a legal proceeding.

Subpoena duces tecum—An order from a court directing a person to produce documents in his or her possession.

Subrogation—Substituting one person for another with reference to a lawful claim, demand, or right.

Summons and complaint—The initial documents required to start a lawsuit.

Testator—One who makes a will.

Theft—Taking of property without owner's consent. Popular name for larceny.

Tort—A private or civil wrong or injury.

Trespass—An unlawful entry upon the property of another.

Uniform Anatomical Act—An act concerned with the giving of one's organs at the time of death.

Vicarious liability—Holding a person or entity liable in monetary damages for the negligence of another.

Will—The statement of a person regarding the manner in which he or she wishes to give his or her property to person(s) after his or her death.

BIBLIOGRAPHY

GENERAL REFERENCES

Black's Law Dictionary, 6th Edition, West Publishing Co., St. Paul, MN, 1991.

Code of Federal Regulations, 42 CFR, Part 430 to end, 10-1-98, Public Health.

Fiesta, Janine, *Legal Implications in Long Term Care,* Delmar Publishers, Albany, NY, 1997.

MacDonald, Michael, Meyer, Katherine, and Essig, Beth, *Health Care Law*, Matthew Bender, New York, 1993.

Strauss, Peter, Wolf, Robert, and Shilling, Dana, *Aging and the Law*, Commerce Clearing House, Chicago, 1990.

CHAPTER-SPECIFIC REFERENCES

Chapter 2

Kionka, Edward J., *Torts in a Nutshell*, West Publishing Co., St. Paul, MN, 1992.

Chapter 3

Chappell v. Odd Fellows Home, 136 A 2d 72 (1957).

Connelly v. Methodist Home of the District of Columbia, 190 A 2d 550 (1963).
Ferrand v. Redington Memorial Home, 270 A 2d 871 (1970).
Fidelity Union Trust Company v. Reeves, 129 A 922 (1956).
First National Bank v. Methodist Home for the Aged, 309 P 2d 389 (1957).
General German Aged Peoples Home v. Hammerbacker, 3 A 678, 54 Amer Rep 782 (1889).
Gold v. Salem Lutheran Association, 347 P 2d 687 (1959).
Henry Keep Home v. Moore et al., 176 P 2d 1016 (1954).
Old Men's Home v. Lee Estate, 4 S 2d 235 (1941).
Stiegelmeier v. West Side Deutscher Fraun Verun, 178 NE 2d 516 (1961).
Wilson v. Dexter, 192 NE 2d 469 (1963).

Chapter 4

Doxey v. Riverside Guest Care Center, 520 So 2d 1118 (1987).
Helman v. Sacred Heart Hospital, 644 P 2d 605 (1963).
Hicks v. New York State Department of Health, 570 NYS 2d 395 (1991).
Kalmus v. Cedars of Lebanon Hospital, 281 P 2d 872 (1955).
Poor Sisters of St. Francis v. Catron, 435 NE 2d 305 (1982).
Russell on Behalf of Wunstell v. Kossover, 634 So 2d 72 (1994).
Woodlawn Infirmary v. Byers, 112 So 831 (1958).
Zucker v. Axelrod, 527 NYS 2d 937 (1988).

Chapter 5

Corporate Liability, 74 AM JUR 2d Torts (1995), 18B AM JUR 2d (1995).
Evans, L.S., "Tying Down the Elderly: A Review of the Literature on Physical Restraint," *Journal of American Geriatrics Society*, 37, 65, 1989.
Johnson, S.H., "The Fear of Liability and the Use of Restraints in Nursing Homes," *Law, Medicine and Health Care*, 18(3), 18, 1990.
Crawford v. Long Memorial Hospital, 66 SE 2d 63 (1951).
Czubinsky v. Doctors Hospital, 1988 California Reporter 685 (1983).

Deerings West Nursing Center v. Velma Pander Scott, 787 SW 2d 494 (1990).

Eugene Merriman v. New York State Department of Mental Health, 282 NYS 2d 167 (1976).

Erie Care Center v. Ackerman, 449 NE 2d 486 (1982).

Golden Villa Nursing Homes v. Smith, 674 SW 2nd 343 (1984). (Not summarized in text.)

Helen H. Fields v. Senior Citizens Center, Inc., 528 So 2d 573 (1988).

Holtforth v. Rochester General Hospital, 105 NE 2d 610 (1952).

Kildren v. Shady Oaks Nursing Home, 549 So 2d 395 (1989).

Knutson v. Life Care Communities, Inc., 493 So 2d 1133 (1986).

McGillivray v. Rapides Iberia Management, 493 So 2d 819 (1986). (Not summarized in text.)

Montgomery Health Care Facility v. Ella Ballard, 565 So 2d 221 (1990).

Nolan V. Booty et al. v. Kentwood Manor Nursing Home, Inc., 483 So 2d 634 (1985).

Penland v. Brentwood Rehabilitation Center, 260 SE 2d 678 (1979).

Slocum v. Berman, 439 NYS 2d 967 (1981).

St. Vincent's Hospital v. Crouch, 292 S 2d 405 (1974).

William N. Jones Memorial Hospital v. David, 553 SW 2d 180 (1977).

Williams v. Orange Memorial Hospital, 202 S 2d 859 (1967).

Chapter 7

Allen, James E., and Miller, Jerome M., *NHA College Directory and Licensure Requirements*, NAB and University of North Carolina LTCA Teaching Resources Project, Washington, DC, and Chapel Hill, NC, 1995.

NAB Study Guide, 3rd Edition, National Association of Long Term Care Administrators, Washington, DC, 1997.

Chapter 8

Final Rule: Health Care Programs and Fraud and Abuse Amendments to OIG Exclusion and CMP Authorities Resulting from PL 100-93 57 Federal Reg 3298, 1992. Codified at 42 CFR PTS 1001 to 1007.

Kannensohn, Kim, "New Law Stiffens Penalties for Fraud and Abuse and Sets Up Advisory Opinion Process," *Bender's Health Care Law Monthly*, September 1996.

Special Fraud Alert, Office of Inspector General, Department of Health and Human Services, May 1989.

Wilken, Gordon, "Health Care Fraud," *U.S. News & World Report*, February 1992.

Darling v. Charleston Community Hospital, 211 NE 2d 253 (1965).

Feuereisen v. Axelrod, 473 NYS 2d 870 (1984).

Frye v. Kaladjian, 617 NYS 2d 1003 (1994).

Hipp v. Hospital Authority of the City of Marietta, 121 SE 273 (1968).

Sanchez v. Board of Examiners of Nursing Home Administrators, 461 NYS 2d 920 (1983).

Sreter v. Board of Examiners, 460 NYS 2d 468 (1983)

Terrel v. Cockrell, 286 SW 2d 950 (1956).

42 U.S.C. §1320 A-7G.

42 U.S.C. §1395 nn.

31 U.S.C. §3729.

42 U.S.C. §1320 A-7A.

56 Federal Reg 3595B (1991).

57 Federal Reg 3348 (1992) Codified at 42 CFR §1003.109.

57 Federal Reg 3347 (1992) Codified at 42 CFR §1003.106.

Chapter 9

Anderson, Howard J., and Kenny, John J., *Primer for Labor Relations*, Bureau of National Affairs, Washington, DC, 1984.

Chester, Charles Frederick, "Union Strikes, Patient Abuse, and Legal Protection for the Nursing Home," *Journal of Long Term Care Administration*, ACHCA, 18(2), 1985.

Fair Labor Standards Act of 1938, as Amended, Department of Labor, WH Publication 1318, May 1984.

Handy Reference Guide to the Fair Labor Standards Act, Department of Labor, WH Publication 1282, 1983.

Holley, William, and Jennings, Kenneth, *The Labor Relations Process*, Dryden Press, Hinsdale, IL, 1980.

Leslie, Douglas L., *Labor Law in a Nutshell*, West Publishing Co., St. Paul, MN, 1991.

Public Law 99-150, Nov 1985, Amendment to the Fair Labor Standards Act, Department of Labor, WH Publication 1318-A, May 1986.

Staines, Graham C., and Quinn, Robert D., "American Workers Evaluate the Quality of Their Jobs," *Monthly Labor Review* 102, January 1979, pp. 3–2 (survey data courtesy of the Center for Political Studies, University of Michigan).

Monthly Labor Review Online, Bureau of Labor Statistics, Washington, DC. http://stats.bls.gov/opub/mlr/mlrhome.htm.

American Hospital Association v. NLRB, 899 F2nd 651 (1990).

NLRB v. Jones and Laughlin Steel Company, 301 US 1 (1983).

University Nursing Home et al., 168 NLRB 53 (1984).

Chapter 10

Public Law 101-508, Nov 5 1990, (PSDA-90), Omnibus Reconciliation Act, 1990, Sections 4206 and 4751.

Uniform Probate Code, ND Century Code, Title 30.1-01-01 (1-101), Allen Smith Co., Indianapolis, IN, 1992.

In Re Kowland Estate, 18 NW 2d 290 (1945).

In Re Larsons Estate, 71 p 2d 47 (1937).

Patterson v. Imbsen, 194 NW 842 (1972).

Chapter 12

Interpretive Guidelines, 42 CFR, Part 430 to end, Sec 488.115, Chap IV, (10-1-98).

Index

ABOUT THE AUTHOR

Peter J. Buttaro is an attorney at law and a health care administration educator. He received his AB in psychology from Syracuse University in Syracuse, New York, his masters degree in health care administration from Northwestern University in Chicago, Illinois, and his doctor of law from Suffolk Law School in Boston, Massachusetts.

Mr. Buttaro has taught long term care administration and legal aspects of health care administration at Northeastern University in Boston, Massachusetts, and at Presentation College in Aberdeen, South Dakota. He has been a guest lecturer and presented workshops nationally at leading universities and state health care associations. He has authored three books: *Principles of Long Term Health Care Administration, Step by Step Guide to a Higher Score on the NAB Exam* and *Legal Manual for Long Term Care Facilities*. Over the past 25 years, these books have been used as basic texts in university and college programs and individually for national licensure of nursing home administrators.

Mr. Buttaro is a fellow of the American College of Health Care Executives and a subscribing member of the National Board of Examiners for Long Term Care Administrators. He is past president of the board of directors of the Benedictine Living Centers, an organization that owns and operates nursing homes and related facilities in several Midwest states.